"Saving $621 (50%) the first month and $860 (67%) the second month lets you know I'm sold on Jil's methods. With eight children, I used to spend about $1260 a month and worry about running out of money. Not any more. We eat well and nutritiously. And our savings have allowed us to store enough to cover an emergency. I now feel secure."
—Linda Phillip

"I now have three times more groceries in my cupboards than before, on the same budget."
—Patty Turner

"I really enjoy your ideas and the excitement they give me to save money. I had an exciting experience—I bought clothes for my 16 month old daughter the way you told me. I bought them all for only $27.00, but the regular price added up to $110.00. I felt great!"
—Lois Jean Spinder

"I have always fed my family with good nutrition in mind, but I felt I was paying too high a price. I was never able to stock up on food storage. My first month using Jil's methods I was able to buy three cases for storage, stock my freezer full of meats, have an abundance of fresh produce and still had money left over. It's exciting!"
—Christina Thomas

"I graduated from the University in Home Economics twelve years ago and have been teaching in that field ever since. I decided I was in need of brushing up on my consumer skills and chose the Abegg method of doing just that. The information has not only reinforced what I had already learned, but increased my knowledge through the Abegg's experience. I strongly recommend this book!"
—Vyki Anderberg

"These money saving ideas are GREAT! I've begun to have real success and it's such a good feeling! I am anxious to pass these saving ideas on to my married daughters."
—La Fae Pyne

Eat Well...
Stay Well...
SPEND LESS!

Build your
Immune Power...

Double your
Buying Power!

Jil Abegg

Published by:

 CAM Publishing Company
513 West Kwanzan Circle
Orem, Utah 84058

Distributed by:
Granite Publishing and Distribution, L.L.C.
270 South Mountainlands Drive Suite 7
Orem, Utah 84058
(801) 229-9023 • (800) 574-5779 • FAX (801) 229-1924

ISBN: 1-57636-045-8
Library of Congress Catalog Card Number: 97-61862
Production by: SunRise Publishing, Orem, Utah

ABOUT THE AUTHOR

Jil is an author and lecturer. She has previously been a professional secretary and teacher with a Bachelor of Science Degree in Business Education and minor in Business Management and Accounting. She is a successful homemaker and is active in civic, church and parent-teacher associations.

Over the years, Jil has shared these skills in saving money and effective home management with hundreds of interested persons in classes and seminars.

Jil and her husband, Myrlon, are parents of eight children. Together they have learned many of the "ropes" in the "school of hard knocks" and have originated or experienced and refined first-hand the money-saving ideas in this book.

Jil is available for seminars and Relief Society presentations. Contact her through:

CAM Publishing Company
513 West 513 West Kwanzan Circle
Orem, Utah 84058

DEDICATION

This book is dedicated to all those who, with me, know the anguish and struggle of trying to make ends meet—putting enough food on the table and clothes on the backs of their families—wondering all the while just how they are going to make it until the next payday and if it will ever be possible to get "on top."

With the assurance that it can happen, this book is dedicated to you.

To my husband, whose idea it was to put it in book form. To my children who have survived my experiments and have gone along with the plan.

Wondering...how to stretch the paycheck to pay all those bills?

Don't give up!
Here are numerous power-packed, proven ways to help you eat well as you save money in grocery and household shopping!

As for poverty, no one need be ashamed to admit it; the real shame is in not taking measures to escape from it.

— *Pericless*

INTRODUCTION

As inflation causes the Government Consumer Price Index to continue to rise, thus driving up the cost of food, clothing, and household goods, American consumers approach the twenty-first century finding it increasingly difficult to supply family needs and manage household budgets.

There is increasing evidence that consumers need to understand nutrition/diet, and its affects on the human body as the American immune system fights an uphill battle.

There is a great need for the consumer to become expert in running their household economically without sacrificing nutrition. HOW TO PUT ALL THE ECONOMICS, NUTRITION, AND HOUSE-HOLD EFFICIENCY TOGETHER IS WHAT THIS BOOK IS ALL ABOUT.

Books begin as ideas, bits and pieces of information that have been worked and reworked, put on the shelf, removed and worked again. Such is the case with this book. It began years ago as my husband and I worked to develop ways of surviving financially.

With a family of ten, we've had to create not only a practical economic philosophy, but ways and means to make ends meet. Of necessity, we came up with many innovative shopping skills that have enabled us to live very well on a modest income. We've found that it is not necessarily a matter of how much income we bring into our household, but we've learned how to save money by creating greater buying power from the money we do have.

We have a comfortable home and lifestyle. We are often asked how we do it. Back-fence discussions and telephone conversations led to numerous requests for me to share my methods with women's groups interested in saving money while yet providing tasty, attractive and nutritious meals on a "shoe-string."

As the number of classes and seminars increased, so did our reservoir of helpful information. I could no longer cover it all in an evening or two. Eager participants required more ideas, more "how to" information and materials. Many consumers have testified to the power of this information as they have implemented the ideas into their daily lives. Many say the information has "saved them economically." So, the idea of a book was born. Simmering on the back burner for months, even years, the idea slowly responded to the cry for action. Now, after hundreds of hours in the preparation, it is a reality.

The book, *Eat Well... Stay Well...* SPEND LESS!—*Build Your Immune Power... Double Your Buying Power!* is just what it says. This book shows the consumer how to get more BUYING POWER into their shopping dollar—teaching them to become BUYERS rather than just shoppers. This book helps the consumer set up their own HOME STORE as they become a BUYER, putting them in CONTROL of their hard-earned dollars. And of great importance, the book helps the consumer to become a preventative "home nutritionist."

Nutritional information, nutritional menu plans and over a hundred recipes are included. The recipes are directed to people who realize that a diet change is possibly necessary, but do not wish to make such a drastic life-style change that the diet is all consuming and many foods they have eaten for years must be replaced with a "wheat and soy burger" vegetarian-type diet. The majority of these recipes are nutritious and healthy. They include many whole grains, legumes, nuts, seeds, fruits, vegetables, and some meats. But there are some desert recipes which do not cut out all the sugars and fats. We feel it is more important to incorporate more "good" foods into a diet and not worry so much about taking out all of the "bad" foods. As we do so we find that many of the less-healthy foods then fall by the way side.

The recipes given in this book can be made as nutritious as one wishes by substituting and replacing, which is what we do all the time. Being realistic, a good cookie has sugar and butter in it. But the cookies can be made with whole wheat flour, whole grain oats, nuts, raisins, etc. Take the basic recipe and create what you wish. Being realistic and raising eight children has helped me to know that we are not going to go through life eating a totally perfect and healthy diet. However, we can do more good things for our bodies than bad, and replace better foods with the less healthy foods. This type of living helps keep the immune system pumped up, thus eliminating the use of antibiotics, drugs, and continual trips to the doctor.

This is a book about SAVING BIG MONEY—about becoming more knowledgeable about the importance of good nutrition—about freeing up a person's valuable time as they manage their household as a business.

THIS IS A BOOK WHICH HELPS THE CONSUMER ESTABLISH EXPERTISE IN COMPETING WITH THE SELLER IN A KNOWLEDGEABLE AND EXPERT WAY—THUS THE CONSUMER IS NOT LEFT TO THE MERCY OF THE MERCHANT AND SALES PSYCHOLOGY.

The book has been written in a manner that is easy to read and understand for the purpose of helping you become a better "home nutritionist" and helping you save money. First-hand experience and the development of a skillful shopping philosophy provide the proven ways of saving big money and enjoying a more healthful life style.

The book is arranged in six parts, all devoted to the saving of money and time, the development of effective home management, and becoming more knowledgeable about good nutrition. The center of action is Part One where ideas of money saving in grocery, household, and clothing shopping are presented. Some of you may be aware of and use some of the ideas, as we all have our favorite ways to save extra money; but many of these wonderful ideas will benefit you generously. We talk about a total "buying picture", a way to run your home as a business, allowing you, the consumer, to be in charge of your money and double your buying power.

The money savers are presented under the general headings of "Get Ready,... Get Set,... And Go!" indicating a helpful sequence of knowledge, preparation and action. Additional tips follow in Part Two. We know the money savers work. We have proven them ourselves, many times over. And many happy students of our money-saving "shopology" frequently inform us of the turn for good in their lives. Frustration has changed to excitement. Hope overcomes discouragement. Success replaces despair. Yes, they do work, these money-saving ideas. We guarantee it, 100 percent.

Eat Well... Stay Well... SPEND LESS! is more than specific "how-to's". In this book, we strive to create an overall savings and nutrition sensitivity and awareness.

The marketplace is a vital part of our society and has provided us a standard of living unsurpassed. We don't discredit the businessman, the salesman, nor big business and industry that have developed our modern miracles of equipment and know-how. Nor do we begrudge them their fair share, even a generous share of the rewards for their ingenuity.

But we do insist that we who are blessed with modest incomes have the right and deserve the opportunity of retaining as much of our hard-earned money as possible. In reality, our vigilance in the matter provides the competition and conscience that spurs the business and industrial world to improve its products and services while lowering prices in the process.

Consider this analogy. The marketplace can be compared to a battlefield with the outcome of the war depending on how successfully we fight the battle of the budget.

Or a game of competitive athletics, the object of the game being to win and win as big as possible. The game is enjoyable for its own sake, but immensely more so if won. The contending coaches teach their teams everything they know. They study, research, hire technicians to assist, develop skills and special techniques, drill and rehearse. Win or lose, each team scrutinizes its moves, its mistakes and its success, all to assure continual improvement. Most of this preparation is kept, if possible, under cover, screened from opponents' curiosity.

So it is with shopping. The grocer studies, researches, practices, analyzes, hires technicians and advertising experts. In short, he spends fortunes developing methods to persuade you to do business with him on his terms. We believe the shopper must be equally as studious, diligent and wise. After all, it is her/his money at stake.

The intent of this book is to help you, the shopper, become a buyer, keeping as much of your income as you possibly can while eating the best diet for optimum health, and spending less time doing all of this.

There are many books on the market dealing with menus, diets, nutrition, how to shop and save, and other subjects similar to those found in this book. Some claim methods for feeding your family on a trifle, but require a change of lifestyle and eating habits so radical that they lose their appeal and practical effectiveness.

Our money savers are unique in that they allow you to retain or determine any eating preference you wish. At the same time, however, there is an underlying emphasis on food quality, appeal, and nutrition. Recurring throughout the book are methods of saving you time and improving your ability to successfully manage your home. All this and big savings too.

Prices may vary widely and change rapidly. In a fluctuating economy such as ours, prices are not likely to remain the same for long. For that reason, current market prices may differ from those quoted in the book. Specifics change; principles endure.

With increased natural disasters affecting food costs, with inflation continuing to rise, with the breakdown of the American immune system and its ability to ward off the new diseases attacking the body, with increased need for time-household management, where is the consumer to turn? Hopefully not to frustration, but to HAVING THE ABILITY TO CONTROL THEIR OWN ECONOMIC DESTINY WITH CONFIDENCE BY IMPLEMENTING THE IDEAS AND METHODS FOUND IN THIS POWERFUL HOW-TO BOOK.

Enjoy reading the book. You will be happy with what it can do for you. Apply its principles to all your shopping, not just groceries.

Best wishes for your successful buying as you *Eat Well... Stay Well...* SPEND LESS!

— Jil Abegg

Table Of Contents

PART ONE

PROVEN WAYS TO
SAVE BIG MONEY SHOPPING

Get Ready . . .

Money Saver One

ADVANTAGES OF THE NECESSARY NEWSPAPER

Where and when can the best buys be found?
Let your fingers do some walking before you ever set foot
inside the store.

Becoming a "smart shopper" is what saving money is all about. To be a smart shopper one must be informed. How is it accomplished? Several ways, really. Four or five basic texts are at your fingertips— your local newspapers, mailers, radio and TV advertisements, and the yellow pages of your telephone directory.

Stores earnestly compete for your business. They use a number of enticements, one being the "leader," a product the store sells as a lure. The store advertises the leader to entice you in with the hope you'll do the rest of your shopping there. Statistically it works. Once in a store, a consumer will generally purchase more than he went in for.

With saving money as your goal, you will read the newspaper ads from all or several of the local stores and make a list of only those items you need which are leaders or on sale. You'll then shop these stores buying ONLY the sale items at each. The remainder of your shopping list you'll purchase at the store whose prices are lower over-all.

Become familiar with the classified ad section of the newspaper. Here you can find many great savings just by checking the various columns such as the "farmers' column" or the "fruit and vegetables column," or the "miscellaneous for sale column."

You'll soon find that for saving money, the newspaper can be one of the best helps you have. It is a basic tool for many of the money savers covered separately in the book. A wise shopper cannot afford to be without a newspaper. In a short time it will pay for itself many times over.

An increasingly popular means of advertising is the mailer which comes to each household via the mails. It is often considered junk and a waste of time, discarded immediately without even a glance being given it. For a wise buyer to know what is going on in the market-place, the mailer, too, is an important tool. Use it. Some stores advertise through the mailer exclusively, causing you to easily miss excellent buys unknown to you without it. Don't discard it without reading its content. It could cost you valuable savings.

Radio and TV advertising can also be informative. Their greatest drawback is the dependence upon memory. But they can alert you to excellent savings.

A little used tool for smart shopping is the yellow pages of your telephone directory. Search out the headings of interest to you—food, clothes, etc. Wholesalers, outlets for factory seconds, and used, as-is and slightly-damaged goods outlets are often listed and can offer excellent buys.

"To buy or be sold" is the name of the shopping game. Everyone plays. Both buyer and seller meet in the market place for a specific purpose. For the seller the purpose is to distribute goods and services for a profit. As a buyer, you should have as your objective the filling of your needs and wants with the best product at the lowest price. Each party is primarily concerned with his own welfare. The success of the game depends entirely on the skill, knowledge, and determination of the players.

Your success as a shopper depends on how well you know your needs and wants and your ability to locate and purchase the best product to fill that need as opposed to allowing the salesman to sell you on the worth of a product based on his interpretation of its benefits. To accomplish this advantage, you must be informed. Take time to read the newspaper and mailer ads, shop the yellow pages, check out the seconds outlets and listen to radio and TV advertisements. This is how you will know where to go for best quality and lowest prices, rather than just jumping into the car and driving off to the nearest store to make a possibly unwise and too costly purchase.

"Clip 'n clip." You'll want some organization in the use of ads. Cut the ads out and attach them to your clip board. When you are ready for your shopping trip, spend a few minutes studying the various ads you've collected. Jot down the items of interest, listing them according to the stores where featured, and write the price quoted in the ad. Keep the ads on your clipboard with this list of stores to shop and items to buy. List and shop the stores in the order of closest store first. This will minimize criss-crossing town and will save you time, frustration and gas money.

This little bit of thorough preparation makes a smart shopper. It puts you intelligently in control of your shopping and your time and will make possible significant savings. Simply having the ads with me often saves me money. Surprisingly, the checkers frequently forget or are unaware of discounts, or the cash registers have not been programmed for sale discounts. When this situation arises, the checker obviously charges the regular price until I point out the discrepancy, showing the ad in my possession.

You must be aware of prices. Be prepared. It really doesn't require much time, just a little organization. Know what a good buy is. A little time with the tools we've discussed will do wonders for you. Remember, it's your money. You be in charge. You be the expert. Buy according to your intelligent preparations. Do not allow yourself to submissively be sold, ignorant and helplessly subject to the desires and whims of the clerk.

Money Saver Two

MAKE RECORDS THE RULE FOR YOUR HOME BUSINESS

What's in storage? How much have you spent?
Just look at your records!

If you were managing a business, you wouldn't do it haphazardly. You would faithfully keep accurate and complete records of your expenditures, accounting for everything you purchase. This is the way you want to manage your home—as a business. It is your business.

To begin with, it's a good idea to have a notebook or loose-leaf binder where you keep your records—such things as menus, shopping lists, prices from week to week, a running account of what you have in your food storage, your seasonal shopping needs, ads, etc.

You will put in this book everything that will help you operate your home business. For instance, you might post your weekly or monthly purchases so you know whether you're staying within your budget; so you'll know where all your money's going (or has gone!). By keeping records, you soon learn what is a good buy and what isn't. Then when you see a special in the paper, you'll know if you're really saving money by purchasing it.

You could also keep your menus and shopping lists for the week or month. When you go shopping, buy ONLY those items on your list.

In this business of shopping, you can't be just "part-smart." You must understand exactly how a store tries to persuade you to spend your money. Store managers are businessmen, and smart. You are a business person, too. And you've got to be smart so you are the one in control of yourself and your money. This requires an organized plan. You must know *what* you need, *when* you need it and *how* you're going to get it. An organized food and household record can help you do this.

Know your business and the grocer's. It will mean dollars in savings and will put you in control of your shopping dollar.

Suggested Materials for Food and Household Records...

- Notebook or loose-leaf binder, filler, and tabs
- Card file box, cards and index
- File cabinet (at least a cardboard, single drawer)

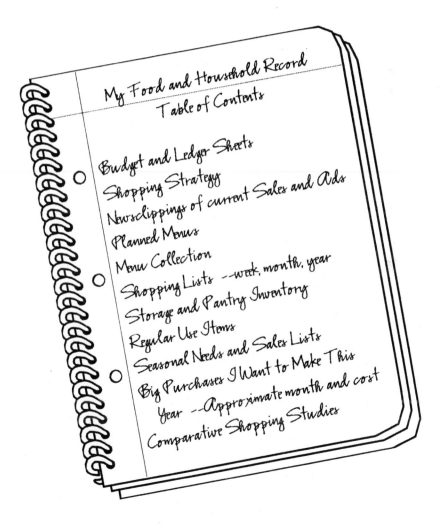

My Food and Household Record
Table of Contents

Budget and Ledger Sheets
Shopping Strategy
Newsclippings of current Sales and Ads
Planned Menus
Menu Collection
Shopping Lists --week, month, year
Storage and Pantry Inventory
Regular Use Items
Seasonal Needs and Sales Lists
Big Purchases I Want to Make This
Year --Approximate month and cost
Comparative Shopping Studies

Money Saver Three

MENU MAGIC: USE WHAT YOU BUY AND BUY WHAT YOU USE

*Menu plans are a must if you want to avoid running
out of money before you run out of month.
Plan for nutrition as well as economical buys.*

Being a smart shopper is not only knowing what the good buys are and where to find them, but also knowing what you need to buy. That's where menu planning comes in.

One of the first things I do when planning my menus is to study the weekly and biweekly grocery store ads. That way I know what good buys are available. Next, I need to know what I have available in my food reserves or what I have on hand that should be planned into the menus. If I've been shopping wisely, the items in my food reserves will be those which we want, need, and most often use as a family. An important part of menu planning is to "use what you buy and buy what you use."

I also take into consideration the time of year and the types of food items that are available at a good price. In the summer and fall growing season, I include in my menus the available produce from our garden or local fruit and vegetable stands.

Some people plan menus by going through recipe books and planning their meals around dishes which strike their fancy or look good. Planning this way will cause you to pay much more for ingredients. Many times a recipe will call for things which you don't have on hand, requiring extra trips to the store or buying items which you could do without. And that means added expense. Menu planning in this manner doesn't save money. You could even end up spending more than you would otherwise.

Remember, in all your planning, the goal is optimum health—eating to live, not living to eat—and optimum savings. Plan your menus around the Pyramid Guide (six food groups). Serve a variety of foods to provide the needed daily nutrients. You may be tempted to cut the food budget by cutting corners on nutrition, but poor nutrition leads to health problems. I would rather pay for better quality and nutrition in our family's diet than put my money into doctor bills.

To be a wise and thrifty shopper, you must use well-planned menus as part of your strategy. I'll show you how this works for me. Let's say there's a leader on broccoli which I buy. I'll then pull out all my menus which use broccoli, such as chicken and broccoli casserole, steamed vegetables (including broccoli) with cheese sauce, vegetable plate (with broccoli) and dip, broccoli steamed and buttered, etc. I include these broccoli dishes in my menu plans for the next two weeks, or even for the month. Having a second refrigerator, I can bag and tie the broccoli when I get home. That way I'm able to use it over a longer period of time and save paying the higher price when it is no longer a leader.

A good way to keep track of your menus and shopping lists, as well as other food and shopping related information, is to have an organized food and household record. Once you institute such a record, you'll find it indispensable. Saving your menus and including them as part of this record will save you much time and effort as you plan your meals and shop for groceries.

By knowing exactly what you have on hand, in addition to knowing what good buys are available and what you're really going to need, you'll find that it gets easier and easier to be a wise shopper. At first it may seem like extra work or trouble to plan menus ahead of time, but once you start and get in the habit, you'll see that it's worth it in the long run, both time-wise and money-wise!

Remember, for BIG savings, be a wise shopper...

• Use what you buy and buy what you use
• Study the ads in the newspaper
• Know what you have on hand
• Plan your menus
• Develop a shopping strategy
• Organize a food and household record

Money Saver Four

A SHOPPER FOR ALL SEASONS

Use a "seasonal sale" list to plan purchases into your budget, and buy ahead!

Have you ever noticed as you've read the ads that items, food and household, are lower during a particular season than at any other time? These are the seasonal sales which are usually quite consistent and can, therefore, be planned into your buying needs.

It's important that you be aware of these seasonal sales as they come along and that you be prepared to take advantage of them. One way to keep track of the seasonal sales and your family's needs is to keep a list in your food and household record. In one section of that record, you should list some of the big purchases you'll want to make during the year. You can do this with food and other household purchases as well.

You'll find it a great benefit to sit down with your partner, if possible, at the beginning of the year and list your buying needs for the whole year. Keep a running list of stock on hand: amounts, sizes, etc., then you'll have a fairly good idea of your needs for the year. Next to the items you know you need to purchase, make a notation as to the month when you plan to buy them, based on the seasonal sales. Doing this, you'll know what you need and what to watch for in the ads. Wait for those items to go on sale before you purchase them. If you've planned ahead, you'll be prepared.

Use a "seasonal sale" list to plan your purchases into your budget. For example, in our area items such as fresh nuts, seeds, raisins, and coconut usually sell at a lower price in late September or early October. At this time, I buy a large supply to last for the year. When my holiday baking begins in November and December (when these items are usually at their highest), I already have them in my home store ready for use, and I will have purchased them at a lower price, saving many dollars.

Be a shopper for all seasons and you'll be an All Seasons Saver!

Remember, here's how...

- Include in your Food/Household Record a Section
  "Big Purchases I Want to Make this Year"
- Note by each item the month they will likely be on sale
- Watch for them in the newspaper ads
- Example:
  Big Purchases I Want This Year
  Sheets and pillow cases   January
  Nuts   Oct

Money Saver Five

WINNING WAYS WITH LEADERS

*Learn to use leaders to your advantage
and increase your savings.*

Leaders are those products which stores sell near their cost. A grocer advertises leaders heavily. The reason is to make such a good bargain you won't want to pass it up. You'll buy at his store. That's what he wants—you as his customer, now and always. He knows while you are in his store, you will make other purchases. Gaining a customer compensates for selling with marginal profit. That is what leaders are all about.

But you can be clever, too! And you will be clever if you follow this plan:

1. Read the weekly grocery ads in your local paper.
2. Make out your shopping list—listing the different stores by name and the leader items you wish to purchase.
3. Buy ONLY the desired leader items from each store.

By now you're probably thinking that you'll use more gas and time than it's worth in running to all these different stores. Read on.

Suppose you buy two or three (or more) leader items from each store and shop three or four stores. You use a dollar or two for gas. But you save $20 or more! You might even hire a babysitter and pay out a few dollars so you can concentrate on intelligent shopping rather than "hassling" the kids. You save $20 on your groceries minus $2 for gas and $2 for babysitting. Your time was less than two hours. You have just earned yourself $8 per hour, tax free. Is it worth it? Treat yourself to a movie and a meal on the town. You deserve it! And you have earned it!

Money Saver Six

HIGH, LOW OR IN-BETWEEN: COMPARATIVE SHOPPING

Nothing compares with Comparative Shopping when it comes to finding out which store has the lowest prices.

What is comparative shopping? It means going to several local grocery stores, taking notes, checking the prices on items you usually buy, and discovering which store sells what at the lowest price. You become a food-cost detective. Of course, you don't need to do this every time you shop. The prices will stay the same three or four months or longer. Some prices stay the same for six months or more.

By making such a comparison, you become better informed about the cost of different name-brand items in three or four local stores. You might think all these stores will sell an item for about the same price within a few pennies. Not so! For instance, the same name brand can of tuna sells from 69¢ to $1.19 a can; a difference of 50¢ or 42%.

You may have heard advertising grocers claim you'll save more overall buying all your items at their store rather than shopping elsewhere. One such claim interested me. I decided I would like to prove it—true or false—so I made a study of local grocery stores to see which, if any, offered the lowest prices. I discovered this: there are stores which are usually higher priced overall and there are those consistently lower. However, by knowing prices, by reading the local ads and buying leader items, and by purchasing at each store the items which are lowest, my savings can be even greater.

I made another study (see following chart). I visited three stores, shopping name brands only, and purchased items at the stores where they were lowest. Purchasing all items at Store A would cost me $103.67. At Store B, $86.06. At Store C, $84.01. Results: Store B was 17% less costly than Store A, a $17.61 savings.

However, by shopping comparatively and buying only the items which were lowest at each store, my total bill was only $77.99. Comparative shopping came off champion saver, saving me $25.68 off Store A prices, a 25% savings. It took less than an hour and a half of time and cost me 50¢ for gas.

Sure it was more leg work, but the $25.68 savings (minus the 50¢ for gas) was worth it. The 50 items I purchased were for a two-week period.

If I do that every two weeks (which I can) and save over $50 a month on my grocery shopping, it's worth the little extra trouble. I made $25.68 for my hour and a half or $17.12 an hour. There aren't many jobs paying $17 an hour!

What could you do with $50 extra each month? That's $600 a year! It's yours by applying just this one important idea each time you shop.

Now, with this knowledge, which way would you shop? Is 25% a valuable savings to you? It assuredly is to us, and that's why we can eat like kings on a limited budget!

Make your own study. When you become aware of the prices of items you usually buy each month in three different stores, you'll find comparative shopping is worthwhile. Follow this simple method:

1. List the stores you plan to shop.
2. List the items you wish to purchase at the lowest price at each store.
3. Plan your shopping trip so you can start at the first store and buy ONLY those items which are lowest.
4. Go to the next store and do the same.

The gas you use (I traveled four miles) will be minimal. If you've read the ads, planned your menus and decided what and where you're going to buy, the time you spend won't be much. You'll find your savings are worth the little time and effort.

Comparative Shopping (CS) Analysis Form

Product / Size	Store A	Store B	Store C	CS
1 Del Monte Catsup / 32	1.39	1.09	.97	.97
2 Whole Sun OJ / 12	.89	.84	.69	.69
3 Tater Tots OI / 2	1.69	1.41	1.25	1.25
4 Smuckers Grape / 2	1.99	1.76	.99	.99
5 Purex / 1 gal.	.79	.69	.72	.69
6 White King Soap	3.99	3.65	3.85	3.65
7 Lipton Onion Soup	.93	.88	.89	.88
8 Campbell's Chn Ndle	.32	.31	.30	.30
9 Dash / 13 lbs.	10.79	7.23	8.29	7.23
10 Campbell's Crm Chn	.39	.37	.33	.33
11 Campbell's Crm Msrm	.36	.32	.31	.31
12 Bananas	.34	.20	.19	.19
13 Crisco	2.35	2.35	2.32	2.32
14 Jello / 6 oz.	.67	.65	.59	.59
15 Jello / 3 oz.	.35	.34	.29	.29
16 Miller Honey / 5	6.99	4.25	5.69	4.25
17 Bumble Bee Tuna	.99	.88	.93	.88
18 Star Kist Tuna	1.19	.88	.99	.88
19 Old ElPaso Beans	1.09	1.01	1.01	1.01
20 Onions / 1 lb.	.25	.25	.12	.12
21 Milk (Whole) / 1 gal.	1.84	1.74	1.69	1.69
22 Milk (2%) / 1 gal.	1.80	1.70	1.63	1.63
23 Cream / 1 pt.	1.02	.97	.95	.95
24 Cottage Cheese / 24	1.31	1.29	1.27	1.27
25 Tortillas / 18 oz.	.79	.69	.59	.59

	Store A	$103.67
	Store C	84.01
	Difference	$19.66

Comparison Results

Store A	$103.67
Store B	86.06
Difference	$17.61

Product / Size	Store A	Store B	Store C	CS
26 Imperial	.89	.55	.49	.49
27 Cache Butter Solid	2.09	.99	1.58	.99
28 Tomatoes	1.69	1.29	.69	.69
29 Lettuce	.49	.49	.12	.12
30 Oranges / 88	.25	.35	.49	.25
31 Carrots	.25	.20	.29	.20
32 Cucumbers	.50	.30	.25	.25
33 Radishes	.33	.25	.09	.09
34 Green Onions	.33	.25	.09	.09
35 Quaker Oats / 3	1.69	1.55	1.59	1.55
36 Shredded Wheat / 18	1.39	1.31	1.21	1.21
37 Corn Flakes / 12-8	1.69	1.55	1.59	1.55
38 Soda Crckrs Kblr	1.59	1.46	1.45	1.45
39 Graham Crckrs Kblr	1.79	1.57	1.51	1.51
40 Wheat Thins / 16	1.69	1.38	1.42	1.38
41 Mix & Drink / 10	16.59	16.98	13.67	13.67
42 Bordens Cond Mlk	1.30	1.22	.99	.99
43 Sego Canned Milk	.49	.49	.48	.48
44 Comet / 14 oz.	.51	.48	.49	.48
45 Avacado / large	.50	.33	.25	.25
46 Am Beauty Spaghetti / 3	2.59	2.35	1.99	1.99
47 Sugar / 10 lbs.	3.39	2.78	3.35	2.78
48 Mdw Gld Ice Cream / 1	3.96	2.98	2.95	2.95
49 Nalley Pan Syrup / 1	4.59	3.59	3.14	3.14
50 S J Peanut butter / 6	8.38	5.49	6.99	5.49
Totals	103.67	86.06	84.01	77.99

Store A	$103.67
CS	77.99
Difference	$25.68

> Greatest Savings is with Comparative Shopping $25.68—26% Savings.

In a 21 store, 60-item market basket, comparative shopping study made during a recent Savers' Seminar, we found the highest market basket price was $178.12 and the lowest $113.41—a difference of $64.71. This survey included name brands only, as well as fruits, vegetables, dairy products, meats, canned and boxed goods, and paper products.

Another revealing bit of information found was that stores of the same name, but in a different location, had big differences. (Most of us would think the market-basket price should be the same.)

See four store comparison at right:

Store A	$178.12	American Fork	
	142.74	North Orem	
	141.29	Spanish Fork	**Difference $36.83**
Store B	$147.46	Orem	
	136.74		**Difference $10.72**
Store C	$130.64	North Orem	
	123.13	South Orem	
	119.82	Spanish Fork	**Difference $10.82**
Store D	$151.35	Springville	
	131.81	Orem	**Difference $19.54**

Product-Size	Store A	Store B	Store C	CS	Product-Size	Store A	Store B	Store C	CS
1					26				
2					27				
3					28				
4					29				
5					30				
6					31				
7					32				
8					33				
9					34				
10					35				
11					36				
12					37				
13					38				
14					39				
15					40				
16					41				
17					42				
18					43				
19					44				
20					45				
21					46				
22					47				
23					48				
24					49				
25					50				

(Copy this form for your personal use.)

Totals

Money Saver Seven

CHECKMATE AND WIN

*A separate grocery/household checking account
makes all the difference.*

While in the grocery store one day, waiting in line to check out, I overheard the woman at the cash register. Her bill came to $125, a shocking surprise. She had no idea she had put that much into her cart, intending and thinking she had spent only $70. Suddenly she was faced with a difficult decision: put half of her purchases back, or write out a check that would overdraw her account by $55.00.

Have you ever found yourself in a similar situation? I have and I know the anguish it causes. I sympathized with this struggling shopper. Most people are too embarrassed to return the goods and will write the check for the full amount as a quick way out of a bind. Her dilemma was obvious from her mutterings and audible reasoning. She had no means of making up the difference in her checking account, but rather than suffer the humiliation of returning foods, she did as many of us would do and wrote the check for the full amount, only to begin preparing mentally for the inevitable conflict at home—the explaining to her husband why she spent money they didn't have.

How do you handle your grocery money? Do you do as this lady and write checks from your joint account, never knowing what checks your spouse has written and therefore never sure of the balance in your checking account or your grocery allowance?

Or do you carry cash taken from an envelope where you keep your grocery funds? I am a veteran of the envelope method too. I know how many demands there are for a quick and convenient dip into the purse for this and that, especially children's demands. There is always a need and if there is money in my purse, it gets spent. Putting the change back into the grocery envelope is an added nuisance too, and usually doesn't happen.

After suffering this dilemma much too long, my husband and I hit upon an idea that has served us very well. We think it will work as well for you. Our solution was to open a grocery checking account. Paying all our grocery expenses by check eliminates guesswork and clears the air (and the head). We know how much each shopping trip costs. We have a running total of costs for the month, and the balance remaining.

We have mutually agreed upon a monthly budget for groceries and all family expenses. On payday, we simply deposit the food budget amount into our grocery checking account and I am then ready for my shopping activities free of worry and confusion.

Another advantage of the grocery checking account is the record it provides me of surpluses carried over from previous months due to sales and other money savers. For example, during the late summer months there are many good case-lot sales I like to buy, but I can't do it on a single month's budget. However, if I've been able to build up a reserve from the previous two or three months, then I am able to take advantage of buying cases of food at their lowest cost of the year. Having done so I'm able to use this food for several months without further spending which creates a continual build-up of my reserves. Those reserves give me a constant security and ability to take advantage of that "good deal" when it comes along. That's called "buying power," a great position to be in.

So think about it. Consider opening your own grocery checking account. I think you will find it a wonderful help for you. Of all the methods I've tried or been aware of to manage the grocery budget, the grocery checking account is the most practical and successful I've used. It allows me to run my home like the business it is, and as a business method, it saves me time, energy and money.

In summary; a grocery checking account...

• Is simple, easy, inexpensive.
• Gives you exact totals and balances in your monthly budget and your checking account at all times.
• Saves you from the temptation of "dipping" into your budget "kitty."
• Allows you a reasonable and easy defense against the inclination to spend your cash-on-hand to satisfy the many demands of family and self.
• Simplifies shopping, eliminating the worry and frustration of uncertainty of funds.

CHECK BOOK GROCERY ACCOUNT   Month of _____

Check Number	Date	Description	Check Amt	Total Spent for Month	Monthly Balance	Deposit	Checking Acct Balance
	1	Carried over					53.10
	1	Deposit			200.00	200.00	253.10
38	2	Happy Mkt	78.00	78.00	122.00		175.10
39	2	Super Save	12.00	90.00	110.00		163.10
40	11	Ben's Bulk	27.60	117.60	82.40		135.50
41	20	Super Save	45.17	162.77	37.23		90.33
Total at end of month:			162.77	162.77	37.23	200.00	90.33
Carry over to next month:							90.33

Get Set . . .

Money Saver Eight

GOING "SHOPPING" WITHOUT LEAVING HOME

Run out of something while fixing a meal?
Don't hop in the car for a quick trip to the store.
Shop your pantry storage instead!

Have you ever been in the middle of preparing a certain recipe only to discover that you've run out of an item you need, and so make a quick trip to the store to get it? Or, in the middle of the afternoon, you wonder, "What shall I fix for dinner?" You then run to the store for the ingredients.

It's those "quick" trips to the store for an item or two that can wreck havoc with your food budget. First, we pay more for the items we go to pick up because they're usually not on sale at the time. Second, we often buy extra items while there. Have you ever gone to the store for a bottle of milk and returned having spent $25, leaving you without enough money to get through the rest of the month? Don't feel bad. Most shoppers do it several times during the month.

Here's why: If you observe the layout of a grocery store, you'll notice you have to take the "grand tour" of the store to get to the milk. As you tour along, you pass tempting displays that convince you that you just have to have some of this and a little of that. Before you know it you've succumbed and overspent your budget. That's why these quick trips can really kill a food budget, to say nothing of the extra gas and car wear, and the time you have wasted.

These "quickie" trips can be done away with by planning ahead and by utilizing the food storage room. For me, it's quite simple when

I follow this plan:

First, after reading the ads and before my shopping trip, I plan our family's menus. In planning menus, I try to incorporate the store's "leaders" in addition to items we have on hand in our food storage or pantry.

Second, I make up my shopping list and include the items I need to buy in order to prepare my planned menus.

Third, in my food record, I keep a running list of items we use regularly. I make a note when we start running low on them so I can watch for sales and replenish before we've run out completely.

Planning ahead this way prevents having to run to the store for a little of this and that. Everything I need is in my pantry or food storage room. It's like having my own store in my home. Because of this I'm able to go to the pantry storage and find the shelves well stocked with foodstuffs we use year in and year out, and I've bought them when they were on sale. I buy enough to last six months to a year. By using the money-saving ideas discussed throughout this book, I'm able to purchase the items I need in case lots or in bulk. The money-saving techniques I use have provided me with the money to do it.

This is a lot better than having to rely on the grocery store every time I need something. I'm independent—self-reliant. I'm in control and don't have to rely on the grocery store for the things we need when we need them.

Having a fully supplied food reserve also gives us peace of mind in knowing that we're prepared should a crisis arise. We all know at times there will be strikes or shortages in certain foods. Shortages force the price of food to increase. Some items are even unavailable for a period of time. If you already have several months' supply of foodstuffs on hand, you don't need to worry. You'll always be able to feed your family.

Storage Means Security and Savings.

Remember the steps...

• After Checking the ads and your food storage, plan your menus in advance of shopping trips.

- Make shopping lists including items from your planned menus.
- Also include on your shopping lists items from your food record that are running low.
- Stock your pantry storage with goods purchased in bulk or on sale.

Going Shopping Without Leaving Home is having your own store at home—a great way to live.

Yes, it is true! These Money Savers can save you up to 60% of your shopping costs.

Money Saver Nine

DON'T WAIT FOR A DISASTER, OR YOUR STORED FOOD WILL BE

Use foods from your storage in the daily diet so the reserves are being continually used and replenished.

There have probably been times when you've bought large quantities of items such as beans, wheat, or powdered milk, which you haven't used or eaten because your family doesn't like them or you don't really know how to use them.

The main reason you purchased the items was so you'd be "prepared." In the meantime, these items sit for years unused in your pantry storage.

The challenge of having a practical, usable food storage is to store the items you use and use the items you store. Otherwise, even the best storage program will turn to waste, and waste is costly.

If you've decided it would be wise to have on hand such items as beans, wheat and powdered milk, make sure they become part of your family's daily diet. Don't have them around just for preparedness sake. Use them regularly for the benefit of your family. Then in times of emergency, your family will be able to eat as they are accustomed and you'll be able to prepare the foods you're used to fixing.

Whole grains, which are considered very high in nutrition, are ideal food storage items. But they're only valuable if put to good use. To better understand this principle, we need to study nutrition and realize that the reason we're eating is for health's sake, and that in order to get proper nutrition, we need to buy and use those foods which will give us the best possible nutrition for our hard-earned money.

Think of it. one hundred pounds of wheat costs from $18 to $20. How much nutritional value is in that $20 worth of wheat compared to three store-bought pizzas or eight boxes of cold cereal or ten packages of potato chips, all costing about the same. In these days of inflation, we need to make sure that we're getting good nutrition for our money. The goal in feeding our families shouldn't be to send our children to bed just with full stomachs; it should be to ensure their health and energy.

If we see that our pantries are full, and if we use them as we would a grocery store, having planned our purchases and meals around the things we use, the savings will be tremendous. We'll be so much better off, both health-wise and budget-wise. Remember it's not enough to just buy and store items. You need to buy and store the items that you use. And use the items you store. Then your food storage will become a practical benefit in your life rather than just sitting there getting hard and stale waiting for a crisis. In that case it is a crisis.

Remember: Good storage is used storage.

Can now for the
winter ahead!

Money Saver Ten

A GOOD DEAL ON GOOD BUYS:
TELL A FRIEND!

You can't know when every good deal comes along,
and neither can your neighbor. Share the good news
of bargains with a "good deal" group.

"Good things come in little packages." This little Money Saver Ten is potentially one of the greatest money saving ideas we present in this book. It's a matter of sharing.

Occasionally good buys come along that you will be unaware of for one reason or another. You can prevent this loss when you have a "good deal" group.

Here's how it works: Organize a small group of friends, neighbors, or relatives for the purpose of sharing ideas, discussing purchases, and most important, making each other aware of "good deals." It's as simple as that. A brief telephone call will do the job. Just pass the good news along and you won't miss those good buys because you happened to miss the ad.

I have several friends who are "good-buy" conscious as am I. When any of us become aware of something good in the market place, we'll give a quick call to one and she in turn will call another and so on. Thus, we're all informed and can take advantage of good deals.

Another advantage of the group is sharing. Perhaps you can't use a whole case or don't want 100 pounds, but you do want the savings that come with buying in large quantities. The "good deal" members are likely to also want a part of the purchase and its savings. So it's a "good deal" for all.

"Good deal groups" are short on time and effort and long on benefits. Through my "good deal group" alone I've been able to "catch" a lot of wonderful sales just because of a phone call from a friend. This helpful sharing applies to many of the money savers in this book. It is a good deal. So be sure to form your "good deal group" immediately.

Share your good news with your family, friends and neighbors.

Money Saver Eleven

ONE COOL INVESTMENT—SECOND THOUGHTS ON REFRIGERATORS

*Where are you going to put all those leaders
and extra produce? Consider investing in
an extra refrigerator.*

Several years ago we picked up a used fridge for $15. For those 35 years it remarkably has not required a single repair. The savings that refrigerator has allowed our family amounts to thousands of dollars. How's that for returns on a $15 investment? We wouldn't be without a second refrigerator—nor should you. You can't afford to be without one—used or new.

We've already talked about leaders. A second refrigerator really comes in handy here by allowing you to purchase a two to four week supply of perishable leader items. Then you don't have to pay the higher price the next week when they've been marked up again.

Let me illustrate. Thompson green grapes are advertised for 39¢ a pound instead of the usual $1.39. With a second fridge, you can buy a whole case of grapes and store them in plastic bags which have been sealed shut, and they'll last up to three weeks. (Do not wash your produce until you are ready to use it.) This way, your family can enjoy a greater variety and abundance of fruits and vegetables because you're able to afford them. The second fridge is indispensable for capitalization on all sales and savings opportunities.

Right now, you might find a used refrigerator anywhere from $60 up, perhaps less if you're lucky. The secret is to constantly check the want ads in the newspaper and watch for the good buy to come along. I've located many as I've helped friends look for their second refrigerator.

Money Saver Twelve

Another Cool Investment—Freezer Freedom

*A freezer can be a big "budget booster" in this day and age.
Look for a good buy on a used freezer or purchase a new one.
Either way will be worth it for the money it will save you.*

Your freezer enables you to take maximum advantage of food sales, and it makes it possible for you to freeze your own fruits, vegetables and baked goods.

When meats are on sale, that's the time to stock up for the year and store in the freezer. Chicken selling for 39¢ a pound? Buy your whole year's supply instead of paying 69¢ a pound one week and $1.29 another. You'll be paying only 39¢ a pound for the entire year.

During the summer months when fruits and vegetables are plentiful, you'll be able to buy large amounts for less money. Take these surpluses and freeze them. Your family will agree that nothing tastes better than fresh-frozen peaches, strawberries, corn, green beans, etc.

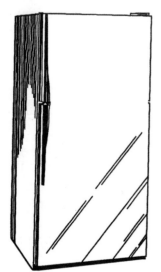

It takes a little work on your part, but the quality and savings cannot be matched any other way.

Having saved on the money-saving ideas used so far, you'll have money to invest in these good buys as they come along. You'll find yourself caught in a pleasant cycle—the more money you save, the more money you have to save. How's that for a change? Feels wonderful, doesn't it?

And the freezer? You buy it the same way—with money these money savers save you. Once you stock your freezer, you'll discover it works for you day after day, actually saving enough to pay for itself in no time at all. A marvelous money saving, budget boosting addition to the family, wouldn't you say? So put a freezer to work for you and see how it can boost your budget—by hundreds of dollars a year!

For maximum efficiency, keep your freezer full. It costs more to keep it cold for one item than when full. So, continually restock.

Use your freezer. It's marvelous for preserving most foods, and we find it enables us to benefit from large quantity purchases. Here are some foods we freeze with success. The list is only a sampling: meats, foul, fish, frozen juices, jams and jellies, baked breads and pastries, ice cream, peaches, apricots, all berries, cherries, fruit cocktail, corn, beans, peas, margarine, butter.

There are two basic freezers—the upright and the chest. Both have advantages and disadvantages. The upright allows better access but loses its "cool" quickly when the door is open. (Cool air falls; hot air rises.) The chest retains its cold air even when open, but requires goods to be stacked, making those on the bottom difficult to reach.

These two Money Savers, Eleven and Twelve—a second refrigerator and a freezer—are a must. They maximize the savings of other money savers presented in this book, and open the door of a whole new world of enjoyable eating and savings.

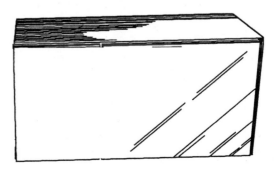

Money Saver Thirteen

PLOTTING A HARVEST: THE FAMILY GARDEN

One of the best hedges against inflation is one you grow yourself. If you don't have a plot, try a pot.

Growing your own vegetables and fruits has become increasingly popular over the past few years with the continuing rise of inflation and desire to "do it yourself." People are discovering that for a relatively small investment of time and money, they can enjoy their own fresh produce.

Of course, the area in which you live has a lot to do with whether or not you can. But people are discovering more and more that they can grow vegetables in very little space—even in the front yard between the curb and sidewalk, or for those in apartments, it's possible to pot indoors or out on your patio.

You might ask if a home garden would really be profitable for the time and expense involved. Brigham Young University of Provo, Utah, in a study of this question, found that a 50' x 50' plot of ground is sufficient to grow enough vegetables to supply the needs of a family of six for summer and winter, if the vegetables were fully utilized— eaten fresh, canned, dried, or otherwise preserved and stored. This size plot produced a total of 1,847 pounds of food with an average of only 2 ¼ hours of time per week for 24 weeks.

The vegetables grown on this plot at fair market price were worth $554.10. (That's figuring 30¢ per pound which is admittedly lower than the present-day market price.) Dividing the number of hours spent into the dollar value of the vegetables amounts to a return of $10.30 per hour, less the expense of seeds, plants, water, etc.

The kinds of vegetables you grow should be determined by your individual family needs and likes. Surplus vegetables grown and not used are a waste of time and money. Some vegetables produce more edible food per foot than others. Therefore, if space and time are limited, select the most productive crops. Some of the best producers for a small garden are table beets, carrots, chard, beans, summer squashes, cabbage, potatoes and tomatoes.

Remember, you can eat vegetables all year round by growing enough to freeze, bottle, dry and pit store.

Vegetables that freeze best are corn, peas, chard, summer squash and beans. Those that pit well in the ground are the root crops—namely potatoes, beets, carrots, turnips, parsnips, cabbage. Those that dry well are peppers, chard, tomatoes and corn. Most vegetables can be bottled. The agricultural extension service near you should have information on the preservation of food.

If you've never planted before, take advantage of the best information available. Booklets on gardening are also available from agricultural extension services. They tell you how and what to plant in your particular area, how to take care of insect problems, weeds—everything you need to know. Be sure to start small. As you get the "bug," you'll want to increase the size and content of your garden.

You'll never know until you try it. Besides being a money-saver, it's therapeutic. There's a sense of pride and accomplishment in knowing that you really grew that beautiful, tasty tomato yourself; that it wasn't picked three weeks ago, trucked far distances, stored in a farmers' market until the grocer bought it and then set in his back room to ripen before finally being put out in the produce section for you to come along and buy it. Nor does it taste the same as picking that succulent tomato ripened on your vine.

For personal fulfillment, terrific taste, superior nutrition and super savings, try gardening. Whether pot, patio, or plot, try gardening. You'll love it.

A home garden can ease the money crunch, add freshness, variety, and nutrition to your diet, and be a lot of fun!

Money Saver Fourteen

PRESERVING FOODS, CONSERVING CASH

Better nutrition, fresher quality, and savings are possible with home canning and freezing. Or, dry it—you'll like it!

With the gardens we've grown, we've always enjoyed a surplus of fruits and vegetables. To make the most of your time and money invested in gardening, preserve your surplus fruits and vegetables for use during the year. Your garden produce can help feed your family year round, not just during the growing season.

To make that possible, your produce needs some special care or preservation requiring little effort for some foods, more for others.

Carrots, for example, can be left in the ground through the winter and spaded out as needed—fresh and firm. A precaution for gardeners in freezing climates to avoid ground freezing: mulch 6 or 7 inches on top of the carrots. Beets will also keep well with this procedure, as will cabbages. However, with cabbages, lay the heads on top of the soil and cover with mulch.

Root cellars: Apples and firm vegetables such as potatoes and carrots store well in cool dry areas. Root cellars, for this purpose, were once very common and may be modified for convenient and successful use in the modern home. Small pits may be dug in your garden, but they must be protected against moisture and rodents. Buried refrigerators and garbage cans are two clever ways of installing a small "root cellar."

Basements are also popular in some areas for food storage. Often a portion of the floor is left uncovered to better serve as the root cellar. Sometimes small basement rooms are devoted to root cellar space, again leaving the floor earthen.

We recommend you start simple and inexpensively, adding more sophisticated methods as you become familiar with the processes.

Freezing is an excellent means of preserving. Freeze those extra green beans, strawberries, etc. Thus, you'll be able to go to your freezer for many commodities during the winter months rather than to the grocery store. Let your freezer work for you by increasing convenience and savings.

Drying is another good way to preserve foods. You can use the sun, oven, buy or make your own dryer or dehydrator. There are some rather inexpensive models on the market. A dryer can pay for itself easily in one season if you take advantage of the fruits and vegetables as grown. Dried foods are good storage items because they take up very little space. Dried fruit and fruit leather make tasty, nutritious snacks for your family. If you've priced dried fruits on the store shelves, you know they can be expensive—as high as $5 a pound. Drying your own saves tremendously.

Bottling fruits and vegetables is easier than you might think, even if you've never done it before. There is nothing like your own canned peaches, raspberries, pears, apricots, tomatoes. The list of cannable food is long. When bottling your own, you are able to control the amount of sugar in the syrup, or you can avoid sugar altogether. There are alternatives available. For instance, you might use apple or pineapple juice for your liquid. These are unsweetened, natural juices and the end result is tasty and nutritious. Honey is also another alternative.

Jams and jellies are very costly and commonly contain excessive sugar. I believe if you get in the habit of making your own jams and jellies, you'll find you can save on your food bill, especially if you purchase your bottles and sugar on sale. A tip on using less sugar in homemade jams and jellies: I find using only half the sugar called for in the recipe and doubling (even tripling) the pectin works well. I also use fructose or a light honey as sugar substitutes. Altering these specifications can cause jams and jellies to be less firm. These syrupy jellies and jams are excellent for use on hotcakes and waffles.

Another nutritional benefit of home canning is the absence of the

many chemicals used commercially for coloring, sweetening, and preserving. Many nutritionists consider these additives very harmful to
the human body. Preserving your own offers much in ingredient control, taste, culinary pride and savings.

Home preservation and canning obviously requires some special
equipment and knowledge. Knowledge can be acquired from books,
friends and relatives and experience. The equipment—bottles, lids,
cookers, and dryers—should be purchased utilizing the money saving

principles stressed throughout this
book, namely sales. These are
items you don't need new. Yard
and garage sales are excellent
sources.

Money Saver Fifteen

MAKING THE MOST OF THINGS YOURSELF

RISING TO THE OCCASION WITH HOME BAKED BREAD

HAVING YOUR CAKE (MIX) AND EATING IT TOO

AND PASTRIES

You can make your own mixes, mix your own cereal,
and bake your own bread—at considerable savings
and satisfaction.

Whether you eat white or whole wheat bread, one fact holds true: You'll save money by passing up the bread at the grocery store and going home and baking it. Perhaps you've never even thought of making your own bread. Perhaps you've tried and failed. Or you've decided you just don't have the time. Whatever your reasons, you may want to reconsider after reading this.

First, think about how many loaves of bread your family eats in one week. Our family of 10 can go through five to ten loaves a week depending on the season and who's home. Right now a loaf of whole wheat bread costs anywhere from $1.00 to $2.50. That averages out $1.75 per loaf. On the other hand, right now you can purchase 100 pounds of wheat for as low as $17. Think how many dozens of loaves you could make with 100 pounds of wheat! Compare that to the nine loaves you purchase for $15.75 at $1.75 per loaf.

I figure that for about 25 cents, I can bake a large loaf of whole wheat bread and save $13.50 each week. That's a savings of $54 per month or $648 a year. Compute your savings on the kind of bread you buy, and you may convince yourself to make your own.

As for being too time consuming, that hardly holds true these days. With the appliances available for grinding flour and kneading dough most of the work has been taken out of making bread. To lessen your time in the kitchen, make two or three batches at a time and freeze the extra loaves for future use. (True, you spend a half day now and again in the kitchen baking; but with the money you save by making your own, it may very well be worth the time you spend.)

As for feeling inept at bread making, many women feel this way because of one or two bad experiences. However, I believe that after trying it a few times, you will soon "catch on" and produce beautiful loaves. There are many excellent recipe books available with helpful tips, making the art of breadmaking almost fail proof.

Nutritionally speaking, there are sound reasons for making your own bread, particularly whole wheat. Consider this: Milling wheat into refined white flour removes significant amounts of the more than 40 nutrients and trace elements contained in the natural whole grain. Law requires "enriched bread" to have some 12 of these nutrients returned. So you can see improved nutritional benefits of making whole wheat bread!

With savings of hundreds of dollars and the improved health benefits of whole wheat, doesn't making your own bread make sense?

Having Your Cake (Mix) and Eating It Too

Have you ever read the ingredients of packaged cake mixes? A typical cake mix label reads something like this:

Ingredients: Enriched flour (bleached flour, niacin, reduced iron, thiamin mononitrate, riboflavin), sugar, dextrose, animal and/or vegetable shortening (contains one or more of the following partially hydrogenated fats: soybean oil, cottonseed oil, beef fat, lard, palm oil) freshness preserved with BHA and citric acid, cocoa (alkali processed) carob flour, modified corn starch, leavening (baking soda, dicalcium phosphate, sodium aluminum phosphate) salt, propylene glycol, mono esters, mono and diglycerides, natural and artificial flavor, guar gum, soy lecithin.

When I make a cake I like to know what's in it. I'm all for using things such as flour, salt, sugar, flavorings, eggs, milk, etc. And reading the ingredients of a typical cake mix warns me there are many chemicals used for sweeteners and preservatives that could pose a serious threat to my health.

I prefer as wholesome and natural foods as possible for all my cooking. Baking is no exception. And the taste: Your taste buds will tell you. There's a big difference in taste and enjoyment with home baked over the packaged mix.

The cost of cake mix is at least 70¢. Making it myself for about 25¢ means a 64% savings of 45¢. Using cake mix once a week amounts to $36 a year. Do it yourself for $13.

If you are nutrition conscious or budget conscious, you will want to consider baking from scratch using your own mixes. Your cakes will be delicious, nutritious and inexpensive.

And Pastries

While on the subject of baking, I'll share a few ideas about making your own pastries.

Because we seem always to be in a hurry with no time to bake, we often find ourselves stopping by the bakery in the grocery store to pick up some cookies here or a pie there. The aromas lure us right over. We think we'll just buy some of those irresistible goodies for dessert. Doing this very many times, we soon find that we're "hooked" and the bakery stop becomes part of our shopping routine.

By scheduling a baking morning every once in a while to bake your breads and pastries, your savings can be $50 or more a month. Think about your shopping habits. Figure the cost and savings that fit your situation. Time is precious these days, so is money, and so is nutrition.

Nutritionally speaking,

we are better off not eating so many sweets. For those interested in lessening your sweets, consider restricting desserts to twice a week. You also improve nutrition when using natural ingredients where possible. Homemade whole wheat cinnamon rolls, oatmeal cookies, date bars, raisin bars, to mention a few pastry possibilities, taste so much better and are better for you.

After reading all about baking breads and pastries, you are no doubt anxious to get started. Do it! Tantalizing recipes await you in the Recipe Section in Part Five.

Money Saver Sixteen

FANTASTIC FIBER—OR— YOU DON'T HAVE TO BE CRACKED TO EAT WHOLE GRAINS AND FRESH PRODUCE

It's less expensive and more healthful to increase the roughage in your diet with fruits, vegetables and whole grains.

Four groups of food have high fiber content—grains, legumes (beans, peas, etc.) fruits, and vegetables. They are truly the fantastic fiber foods.

By purchasing grains in bulk and using them as part of your daily diet, especially in your breakfast meal, your food costs can be cut considerably.

Whole grains are some of the most nutritious items on any breakfast menu, especially if the grain is cracked or rolled just before cooking and eating.

An example of a whole grain that's simple to use is whole wheat. By cracking the whole wheat in your osterizer or electric grinder or by hand, you then cook it as you would any cereal.

Another easy preparation of wheat is putting the whole grain into a little salted water in a Crock-pot just before you retire for the night. Turn the Crock-pot on low, and when you arise in the morning, your cereal is ready! Serve with honey, milk and fruit and I guarantee your family cannot refuse this delicious offering. (Not to mention the fact that chewing cooked whole grain cereal is excellent for the healthful conditioning of your gums and teeth.)

Another excellent grain for breakfast is rice. Grind it in your blender and cook in the top of a double boiler. Ground brown rice cooks up into a light, fluffy "cream-of-wheat" looking cereal. It's delicious served with honey, brown sugar, raisins, bananas, grapes, fresh peaches, or fresh berries, and sprinkled with cinnamon.

Rolled oats, either regular or quick-cooking, provide another superior breakfast dish. Oats offer you other tasty dishes too. Make your own granola for use as a cereal. Add oats to candy, cookies, cakes and other desserts. Purchasing rolled oats in bulk by the 50 or 100 pounds amounts to big savings.

You can also buy your own corn in bulk, grind it into corn meal, or put corn into some of your cereals. There's a boxed cooked cereal on the market which consists of several grains ground together. Why can't we do the same thing? It is much more nutritious and so inexpensive. The savings on buying whole grains will vary. A popular brand of oatmeal sells in the store for $1.69 for a 2 lb. 10 oz. box—a cost of 64¢ a pound. This past month I purchased 50 pounds of oats at 30¢ a pound—$15. If I were to buy 50 pounds of oats in the 2 lb. 10 oz. box over a period of six to nine months, the price I would pay for 50 pounds would be $32. By buying in bulk, I made a 53% savings—$17 extra in my pocket to use for something else. Doing this, you soon have much more buying power for your dollar.

Germade, a cream-of-wheat type cereal, can be purchased in bulk at $7.25 for 25 pounds. This cereal in smaller 10 oz. boxes sells for $1.79. To buy 25 pounds in small boxes would cost $71.60. $71.60 vs. $7.25 is a savings of $64.35!—a whopping 90% savings.

These two examples alone demonstrate the kind of savings possible using whole grains in your cooking, especially buying in larger quantities—bulk. The savings are great and, nutritionally speaking, you're way ahead.

Breakfast is the most important meal of the day. Preparing it from freshly ground grains is one of the best ways of giving your family a head start on the day's demands—a nutrition power-package of health and energy. Packaged cereals lining the shelves of the grocery stores can't compare—nutritionally or in savings! Even products labeled as "rolled oats" or "cracked whole wheat" can't compete in their nutritional value with the value of grains ground fresh. Products begin losing nutrients from the moment they're cracked, and more nutrients are lost in transporting, warehousing and sitting on the shelf. Fortify your family with do-it-yourself nutritious breakfasts.

Eliminate, or minimize, boxed cereals from your shopping list.

Make your own cereals, your own bread, pies, cakes, and pastries using whole grains. The savings are considerable. The nutrition for your family will also be greatly improved—far outweighing the little extra time you may have to spend preparing. Once organized, you'll find it doesn't require much of your week's time.

One caution: If you are not used to eating whole grains, you may want to include them into your diet gradually so your system can adjust comfortably. The fiber in grain sometimes acts as a laxative for those who are not used to it. Therefore, you may want to begin using grains a little at a time.

If whole grains are new to your family, start with desserts and goodies first so they can know how yummy these wholesome foods can be.

There have been many studies on fiber or roughage in a person's diet. Doctors and scientists are discovering that people who consume fiber in the ways we've mentioned have far less risk of heart disease and cancer, especially cancer of the colon. Studies also tell us we can lose weight (without really trying) just by implementing whole grains into our diet.

Fresh fruits and vegetables constitute another of the fantastic fiber food groups and one you'll want to include in your menus, if you haven't already. Their inclusion will offer greater variety and interest in your meals with their rich color and taste. Fruits and vegetables also offer a rich nutritional package of vitamins, minerals and fiber.

It is well to remember that the vitamin and mineral content for all foods is superior when they are fresh. The more processing of a food, the greater the nutritional loss.

By eating foods rich in fiber, we find it more healthful, and we save money on our food bill. Good health compounds savings. Spend less plus eat better equals good health and fewer doctor bills—and more savings.

To make sure I enrich my family's diet with fiber foods, I buy my fruits and vegetables first. I always begin in the produce department. I've read my ads telling me what produce items are featured as leaders. I've planned my menus ahead of time with sale items in mind. Now, I'll buy large quantities of those produce items on sale and include them in my menus for the next several weeks.

When I prepare bag lunches, I make it a point to include fresh fruit every day. I buy large quantities of fruit in season. If the price at the grocery store is too high, I take advantage of the farmers' market (Money Saver Thirty-one) or local fruit stands (Money Saver Thirty-three). Purchasing most fruits by the case, we can afford all we like. Using my buying guidelines, stopping at the produce department first, and buying the leader items, I can fill my basket with as much produce as we can eat. In so doing, I come out of the grocery store with four or five large shopping bags full of produce having paid as little as $20 or $25.

For instance, 10 pounds of bananas at 19¢ a pound for $1.90; a case of 72 oranges for $8.00; 20 lemons at 5¢ each for $1; eight pounds of broccoli at 39¢ a pound for $3.12; 20 pounds of new potatoes at 15¢ a pound for $3; eight pounds of Thompson grapes at 55¢ a pound for $4.40; 10 pounds of yellow delicious apples at 25¢ a pound for $2.50. The total is $23.92 plus tax. For under $25 ($23.92), I've come from the store with a case of oranges and four grocery bags full of produce. That is 104 pounds of fresh produce at an average of 33¢ a pound. This gives me a lot of fresh, delicious, fiber-rich food to enrich my daily menus and lunches.

Little mention has been made of the legumes—beans and peas. The legume is rich in fiber and its basic nutritional content, including protein, and ought to be found in your menus as a means of enriching and adding variety to your meals.

Pinto beans are excellent for extending meat or as a meat substitute. Buy in bulk—25, 50, or 100 pound sacks. They store easily anywhere cool and dry.

Some High Fiber Foods

Legumes	Whole Grains Whole Cereals and Flours	Vegetables
pinto beans	wheat	potatoes
kidney beans	rice	corn
navy beans	oats	carrots
black beans	rye	spinach
lima beans	buckwheat	Brussels sprouts
red beans	corn	broccoli
soybeans	cornmeal	green beans
split peas	bran	beets and greens
black-eyed peas	millet	turnips
lentils	barley	chard
garbanzo beans	triticale	kale
		peas
		lima beans

Fruits and Dried Fruits	Berries	Nuts
apples	strawberries	almonds
apricots	raspberries	walnuts
bananas	blackberries	pecans
dates	blueberries	Brazil nuts
figs	boysenberries	filberts
peaches	cranberries	peanuts
pears		
plums and prunes		
raisins and grapes		

Money Saver Seventeen

HOMEMADE LUNCH EQUALS MORE NUTRITION, MORE SAVINGS

Want your family to have a good lunch at school or work?
Send it with them.

Seven lunches left our home each morning for many years. It may have taken more time than simply handing out money for school lunch, but I've found the savings and added nutrition to be well worth it.

I believe that thoughtfully planned and prepared lunches from home can be more nutritious than purchased lunches, which often contain high amounts of carbohydrates—starch and sugar; more than children require.

Then, there's the cost. In our area a school lunch used to cost $1.10 to $1.25. Figuring $1.10 for six student lunches would mean a cost of $6.60 per day, five days would be $132 monthly or $1188 for the entire 180-day, nine-month school year.

With that same amount I could feed my children better and save half or more by using the shopping methods discussed in this book.

For example, for lunches I bought apples at $8-$12 a bushel. I bought 10 pounds of bananas for $2. By making the bread and sandwich fillings, along with nutritious homemade goodies and adding fresh vegetables (either home grown or purchased on special or at the farmers' market), I made a nutritious lunch for my children for half the money (or less). Notice, I'm talking about top nutrition and less expense. I avoided potato chips, candy bars, or others of the "junk" food category

I might add, it's no longer just children who carry lunches, but adults as well. Recent studies show that the desire to eat well for less has created a new generation of "brown-baggers." Research indicates that twice as many brown-baggers have family incomes of more than $30,000 compared to the rest of the population.

Many are college graduates; and of all the lunch-takers in the nation, only about 25% work in factories. Many are white collar workers who've discovered that by taking their lunch to work, they save from $5 to $10 a day and are able to eat more healthful foods.

Lunch-baggers include businessmen who've had heart attacks and must eat certain foods. Others are working men and women who are dieting or trying to maintain their weight All have discovered that home-prepared lunches can be more nutritious and healthful and can save hundreds of dollars over the years.

Some Brown-Bag Myths

Many people, adults and children alike, don't like to make or take lunches because of the "myths" which have developed surrounding the ideas of brown-bag lunches.

Some of the most common myths are: "It takes too much time to make the lunches," "Sack lunches are boring," "I can only send sandwiches and that gets boring," and "brown bags are ugly."

I want to refute or replace the myths which keep people from making and taking lunches.

To begin with, time is probably one of the biggest factors in not making lunches. Mornings are busy and hectic with everyone getting ready and just barely making it to school and work. Preparing lunches does take time, there's no mistaking that. But there are ways to cut the amount of time you spend so that it becomes worth your while

One way is to make as much of the lunch ahead of time as possible You can mix your sandwich filling and wash and cut vegetables beforehand. Sandwiches can be frozen and popped into lunch bags or boxes as needed.

Another great time saver is to organize your kitchen by creating a "lunch center." This could be a special shelf, drawer, cupboard, even an area in your fridge for lunch foods only. The lunch center holds all your wrappers, bags, peelers, knives, can openers, etc., for easy access so you don't have to go all over the kitchen while preparing lunches. Keep lunch containers, thermos bottles, etc., in the same area. This will save much time.

Next, you want to plan your lunch menus ahead of time. This saves not only time but money because you're able to plan your lunch needs into your shopping schedule. An important part of menu planning is nutritional consideration. Lunch should provide one-third of your required daily nutrition. So when planning your lunch menus, be sure to include something from each of the basic five USDA Pyramid food groups, using the fats, oils, and sweets sparingly.

Incidentally, posting your menus on the family bulletin board allows your children the excitement of knowing what's for lunch.

Now, who said sack lunches have to be boring? For the kids, why not try "fun" menus such as Mexican Fiesta, The Circus is in Town, Robinson Crusoe, Pilgrim Party, Cowboys and Indians. You can use book titles, seasons, holidays, songs, TV shows, etc. as themes for lunches.

You might try substituting names of lunch items on your posted menus such as these for the circus lunch: tiger's milk (milk or juice) elephant's treat (peanuts), trainer's special (sandwich), bare-back rider's special (fruit or raw vegetables). If Pilgrims is your theme, you can use "Squanto Bread," "Indian's Surprise," etc.

Use of color also keeps lunches from being boring or unattractive. Lunch bags don't have to be brown; they come in a variety of colors— white, yellow, green or mixed. Your school-age children may think it's fun to have one of the popular, attractive lunch boxes which can be purchased during the before-school sales in the summer and early fall.

Colored napkins, fruits and vegetables will also brighten the lunches. Snacks of popcorn, seeds, nuts, dried fruits, and cheese and crackers create more interest as do soup, salad, cottage cheese, yogurt, fruit cups, etc. Then, for some special fun and excitement, you might tuck in notes, poems or jokes.

To perk up the sandwich fare try different breads in different shapes, open-face sandwiches, club or triple-decker sandwiches, sandwiches on hamburger or hot-dog buns. Try making your own hoagie sandwiches. Another tasty idea is bagels spread with strawberry cream cheese, etc.

As you can see, there are a lot of ways to keep sack lunches from being dull. I've found that by preparing my family's lunches this way, we enjoy a lot of fun and I feel better about the nutritional content of what they're eating. Furthermore, I'm excited about the money I'm saving.

Money Saver Eighteen

BE A MEAT-CUTTER—CUT OUT THE EXCESS

Protein can he found in fowl and fish, beans and cheese,
as well as meat. Cut down on meat, cut down on expense,
and cut up on savings.

I've said it before. When you shop groceries, don't make your first stop the meat counter! It's possible to "blow" your whole food budget just buying meats. It's a fact you can get along very well with minimal visits to the meat department.

I realize there those who strongly believe in daily meat consumption. However, there are actually many foods containing protein, so it's not really necessary to depend on meat alone for your source of protein.

Nutritionists are finding high-protein diets are not all they've "cracked up" to be. Many medical authorities now suggest we eat less meat, more fowl and fish. They are nutritionally better for us and less expensive.

From the National Academy of Sciences' recent anti-cancer report comes the warning that Americans are eating too much meat, too much protein (especially animal protein) and too much fat. The report recommends we reduce all dietary fats by 25%. That includes meat, dairy products, vegetable fats and shortening. About 40% of the calories in a typical American diet is derived from fats.

Urging us to reduce the amount of red meats we consume, the Academy explains that in cutting back we would fare better eating primarily lean meats, fish and poultry, without the skin. We should furthermore replace the fattier animal protein with low-fat plant protein. Examples are cooked dried beans, peas, lentils, soybeans and soybean products.

Over the past two or three decades high protein has been the general recommendation and practice. The latest research and observations, however, reveal the harmful effects of large amounts of protein in the diet. A dramatic reduction is urged upon us now because it is found that most Americans consume 200% to 400% more protein than needed resulting in serious health abnormalities.

Also recommended is a change in thinking that meats are the only or best sources of quality protein. Protein is generally available in a variety of plant sources as shown in the following chart of some protein-rich foods, animal and plant.

Food	Grams of Protein
Ground beef, 3 oz.	21
Chicken, 3 oz.	20
Pork chop, 2 oz. lean	12
Soybeans, ¾ cup	15
Beans, ¾ cup	11
Milk, 1 cup	9
Peanut butter, 2 T.	8
Cheddar cheese, 1 oz.	7
Egg (one)	6
Rice, ½ cup	5
Nuts, 2 T.	5
Cereal, ½ cup cooked	1-4
Bread, 1 slice	2
Vegetables, ½ cup cooked	1-2

Lentils and cheese are other good sources of protein. I would suggest you include in your recipe file some casseroles and other tasty dishes using non-meat foods. Eating this way is good for your health and your budget.

Our family has eaten far less meat than the "official" daily requirement and we believe we fare better as a result. That's why I stop at the produce section first and the meat counter last when shop. I use an abundance of fresh fruits and vegetables in my family's diet along with ample fish and fowl and a little meat. I enjoy oriental recipes that require very little meat and an abundance of vegetables. I am convinced this is a more nutritious way of eating.

If you are the average American shopper, you will spend about one fourth of your family food budget at the meat counter. This amount can be cut back considerably and comfortably while maintaining or improving health.

Lest I be misunderstood, let me hasten to add that I do enjoy red meats and do include them, sparingly, in my menus. Meat is undeniably a staple of proper nutrition and is overwhelmingly popular and central to our meals. So, a word or two about shopping and saving in the meat department.

When you do purchase meat, consider these money-saving tips to lead you to wise choices at lower prices. The first is to keep in mind that you do not have to pay premium prices for top quality meats. You can select less costly cuts and increase the variety of meats you buy while enjoying significant savings and meats that are tasty, tender and nutritious.

When I'm shopping for any type of meat, I make it a habit to buy only that which is on special or selling as a leader. You can find excellent buys by watching your paper. For instance, chicken legs and thighs were selling at a store for 39¢ a pound. Instead of buying for one meal, I bought several packages and put them in the freezer. When chicken climbs to 89¢ a pound or higher, I'm not in a "have to" buy position. I'm in control because I have several months' worth of chicken in my freezer which I purchased for only 39¢ a pound.

When buying beef, look for the lean cuts. They are fine-grained, firm and bright cherry-red. Bones of young beef are porous and red. Bones of older stock are white and flinty. Vacuum-packed beef will have a darker purplish red color.

With more than 300 different cuts of meat available, it is easy to become confused. The retail meat industry has established a uniform identification for pre-packaged cuts which gives you quick knowledge of the kind of meat, the wholesale name (called primal) tells where on the animal the cut is taken, and the retail name for the cut. "Beef Chuck Blade Roast" is an example. Beef is the animal, Chuck the wholesale or primal cut, and Blade Roast is the retail cut (telling which part of the primal cut). At times the primal and retail names are the same.

At the end of this Money Saver, we have included a simple beef illustration and its cuts. You may find it helpful to become familiar with them.

People may think that buying meat by the carcass is cheaper because it is bulk buying. This is no longer so. Carcass is actually more expensive.

Most meat distribution is now in what is called wholesale cuts or box beef, which means it is packed in large cryvac plastic bags with the air removed to aid preservation. It is less expensive because of mechanical processing in which the formerly unwanted parts, the byproducts, are trimmed from the wholesale cuts. These by-products are no longer considered waste, but bring high prices for the processor. Streamlined processing, good prices for by-products, and you, the meat shopper, get your desired cuts at a lower price.

These box cuts, or wholesale cuts, include short cuts, standing rib, one-sixty round, sirloin tip, sirloin butt, and three-piece chuck, and are all quality cuts.

Summer being the time it is for picnics and barbecues, steaks are extremely popular. With high demand prices rise dramatically. In summer steaks are at their highest. Fortunately, other quality meats are fairly low during the summer and can easily be substituted for steak without loss of taste or quality. These are the front quarter cuts or box cuts, as mentioned above. Short loin and porterhouse are excellent cuts. Most shoppers cannot tell the difference between porterhouse and their favorite T-bone steak.

Some stores have what is called a Surplus Section. Here they sell meat after it has been displayed two days at the counter. It is discounted about 25%; after three or four days it is reduced to 50%.

These meats have lost very little quality or taste. This is an excellent way to enjoy good meats at good savings.

The stores do this, of course, to keep their very choicest cuts out front in view of the public, who want nothing but the best, the reddest, the freshest. Obviously, the customer pays for that extra day or two of freshness which in reality is insignificant.

Freshness can be detected by the experienced eye and when buying in the surplus section, you do want to get the best available. Fresh meat is bright red. As freshness fades so does the color. Remember, though that such losses in a day or two are hardly noticeable.

Storeowners are as interested as you that the meats you buy from them are fresh and of good quality. It would be ruinous for them to have a reputation of selling bad meats. What is more, it is illegal for meat to be "doctored" or treated to make it appear fresh when, in fact, it isn't. For these reasons you can rest assured of quality when shopping established and reputable meat stores.

Another consideration in selecting meat is the trim. When meat is trimmed for display, one-fourth to three-fourths of an inch of fat is left on the cut. The cuts with less fat cost more, of course. However, even though the price per pound is higher, it is usually your best buy because it has less fat. If in doubt, a little arithmetic and comparing will confirm the best buy.

The freezing of meat can also be a factor in quality and savings. Frozen beef lasts well for six months if wrapped in double pliafilm. Single wrapping allows it to dehydrate much sooner. Count on pork lasting only about three months before it dehydrates and becomes dry and loses its flavor.

Become acquainted with the meat cutter in the stores you shop. "Pick their brains." Learn all you can about cuts, detecting quality, freshness and economy. You'll soon distinguish the "selling pitch" from factual information. You can then become expert in the purchase of your favorite meats as in all other purchases.

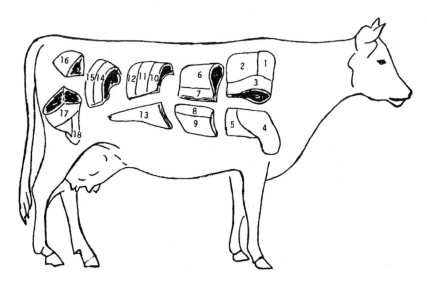

Cuts of Beef

Primal Name	Retail Name
1 Chuck	Ground Beef, Stew
2 Chuck	Blade Roast or Steak
3 Chuck	Pot Roast, Boneless Chuck, Steak
4 Fore Shank	Shank Cross Cuts
5 Brisket	Corned Beef, Fresh Brisket
6-7 Rib	Rib Roast, Rib Steak
8 Plate	Short Ribs
9 Plate	Stew or Ground Meat
10 Short Loin	Club Steak
11 Short Loin	T-Bone Steak
12 Short Loin	Porterhouse Steak
13 Flank	Flank Steak, Stew, or Ground Meat
14 Sirloin	Pinbone Sirloin Steak
15 Sirloin	Sirloin Steak
16 Rump	Rump Roast, Rolled Rump
17 Round	Round Steak, Top Round, Bottom Round
18 Round	Heel of Round, Hind Shank

Money Saver Nineteen

S-T-R-E-T-C-H-I-N-G Meat And Dollars At The Same Time

Get more for your money by using
meat extenders and substitutes.

I've found the use of meat substitutes and extenders such as gluten and TVP to be very helpful in making my meat supply stretch further.

Gluten is a meat substitute which you can make right at home. It's made from wheat and can be used in many appetizing main course recipes. It really doesn't take long to learn how to make it, and the fun part is experimenting and trying to make it taste more like meat.

Gluten comes from the protein of wheat. The wheat kernel contains starch and protein, which separate when wheat flour is prepared and washed with water, leaving a tough elastic substance of long bands or shreds. This is the gluten and consists of amino acids essential for the construction and repair of body cells. A comparison of the protein in wheat, beef and wheat gluten illustrate the difference in amino acid (protein) content.

Essential Amino Acids

100 grams (100,000 milligrams) of . . .

Wheat	equals	56 mg of amino acids	(0.05% of content)
Beef	equals	1,220 mg of amino acids	(1.22% of content)
Wheat Gluten	equals	3,300 mg of amino acids	(3.30% of content)

As you can see, beef is a superior protein over wheat. But when wheat is made, or concentrated, into gluten, it then provides about three times the essential amino acid content as beef with only a fraction of the cost.

A normal body simply does not require heavy intake of meat each day for its protein requirements. Quality protein can be provided by many other foods as well, among them wheat gluten ranks as a champion.

Gluten may be served just as you would hamburger, sausage or roast beef. It can be ground for meatloaf or cut into cubes for stew. Its uses are endless. All you have to do is take the time to read any one of the excellent books available on making and using gluten and then try it yourself. It's another wonderful way to use the wheat which you now are buying in bulk. Wheat itself can also be used as a meat extender if you aren't able to take the time to make it into gluten. I've often used wheat in such dishes as meatloafs, casseroles, chili, etc.—dishes which call for hamburger. I sometimes leave the hamburger out completely or use less hamburger than the recipe calls for, using wheat as a meat extender.

TVP, or textured vegetable protein, is another popular meat extender which can be purchased in bulk and stored for use. It comes in many flavors such as beef and ham and can be used in numerous ways. It's derived from the soybean and is high in protein.

It's important if you're interested in these meat extenders and substitutes that you become informed on their use. Read the books available and follow the instructions.

Meat extenders and substitutes, although high in protein, are not all complete proteins, so other sources should be included with your meals in order to get the complete amino acids, especially if you're

using extenders as your main source of protein. However, I've found that there's enough protein in other foods in our diet, so lack of protein hasn't been a problem.

The fun part of using extenders and substitutes is experimenting and coming up with exciting, flavorful ways to use them in your family's diet. By doing so, you'll find your meat dollar going much further.

Money Saver Twenty

SPROUTING YOUR OWN NUTRITION

You can sprout seeds anywhere. Use them each day
for greater nutrition. It costs so little.

By using sprouts, you get extra nutrition for very little money. They contain substantial amounts of the B Vitamins as well as Vitamins A and C. Because there's very little or no cooking involved in their use, their nutritional value remains high. In addition, the relatively small storage space they require makes them excellent items to store and use.

It's possible to sprout any type of grains, beans or seeds. You need to make sure, however, that you use proper sprouting seeds. Seeds are often treated with fungicides and insecticides. Therefore, be sure to buy only fresh seeds which haven't been chemically treated.

Sprouts are great because you can grow them yourself without a backyard garden plot or even a window box. They can be grown practically anywhere—in the windowsill, on the table, or in the cupboard—using a very simple method. It is worth your while to purchase a small sprouter such as the kind found in many health food stores. Instructions for growing and maintaining the sprouts are included. You can also sprout in a canning jar.

If you're unfamiliar with sprouts and unaccustomed to their use, I suggest you try growing them and adding them to your family's diet for a new adventure in eating. Once you start using them, you'll wonder why you ever did without them.

Here are a few uses...

• Add to your favorite sandwich meat

along with some yogurt or salad dressing for a wonderful sand-wich filling.
- Add to all types of salads.
- Add to soups and stews just before serving.
- Use in oriental cooking. (Many popular wok recipes call for sprouts. It's much less expensive to grow your own rather than to buy them from the store.)

Money Saver Twenty-One

SAY "YES!" TO YOGURT

By making your own yogurt, you can enjoy savings and nutritional benefits.

Yogurt has become a popular addition to the diet of many families. It can be a costly addition, however, when you buy it for a large family.

Many people are discovering that yogurt is an excellent supplement to a well-balanced diet because it's a good source of calcium, protein and riboflavin. The nutrients in yogurt are especially unique because they're nutured in a healthful, easy-to-digest lactic-acid medium. Because of the "friendly" bacteria in the yogurt culture, Vitamin B is manufactured in the intestinal tract of humans consuming adequate amounts of yogurt. The tart taste of yogurt is caused by the acid action of the bacteria upon milk during its coagulation.

Since it is considered high in bacteria count, many doctors prescribe yogurt, especially if the patient is using antibiotics that rob the intestines of the friendly bacteria required to keep those organs functioning properly.

In Part Five of the book are basic recipes from which you can become very creative. From plain yogurt you can make sundaes or Swiss-style by adding your choice of flavors, nuts and toppings. Your family will love frozen yogurt. Excellent books are available on yogurt making, yogurt creations and using yogurt in your cooking.

Making yogurt is very simple. You need only two ingredients—milk and yogurt starter. For the starter you merely use a portion of yogurt on hand or purchased. It can be made with a commercial yogurt maker or pint jars in your oven (even a thermos bottle, thermal blanket or heating pad will do). The important thing to remember is that the temperature must be maintained between 110°-120° for the entire incubation period.

Homemade yogurt is less expensive than commercial and more healthful. It is free from the added sugar and artificial flavors often found in marketed preparations. Making my own yogurt, I can afford to give my family all they want. I know it's good for them because I know exactly what has gone into it.

Yogurt is a delicious addition to many recipes. It enhances rice, wheat and corn dishes and makes an excellent dressing for salads, vegetables and fruits.

If you're counting calories, you'll be glad to know that plain yogurt made with 2% skimmed milk has only 125 calories per cup. That makes it an especially good (and inexpensive) substitute for sour cream which has 485 calories per cup and is quite expensive.

As you can see, yogurt is a nutritious and versatile addition to your family's diet. By making your own, you can have all the yogurt your family desires without threatening your budget.

Frozen yogurt rivals any ice cream!

Money Saver Twenty-Two

DON'T MILK THE BUDGET DRY

How much milk does your family drink? At the current cost per gallon, it would be worth it to try some alternatives like these.

Some families save money by drinking powdered milk—and liking it. Others are unable to do this because they just don't care for the taste of powdered milk. If that's your situation, here are a few suggestions you will want to try.

Use powdered milk in your cooking. I believe you'll find there's little or no difference cooking with whole milk or powdered milk—except for the money savings, and that can be considerable.

Another idea is to mix your milk. Use one-half powdered milk mixed with one-half whole (or 2%) milk, and see whether it pleases your family. The night before you plan to serve it, mix a gallon of good tasting, non-instant powdered milk in your blender. Then add two or three tablespoons of cream and mix well. Next, combine the powdered milk/cream mixture with a gallon of whole (or 2%) milk. Put the containers in the fridge overnight so the milk is cold when served. Your family may decide that milk mixed this way really does taste good. Make this milk mix a regular process and you'll save big money.

Drinking raw milk is another idea. In our area, raw milk used to be about 20-30 cents less per gallon. This may or may not be the case now. You would have to check your local area dairy. It is required by law that all raw-milk dairies be certified; that is, they must have their animals inspected and be able to pass tests for cleanliness and health.

Our children have grown up on certified raw milk, and we have felt good about it. Not only did we save money, but we enjoyed the added benefit of natural unprocessed milk and the bonus of using the cream off the top, thus leaving us to drink skim milk.

Some families go through gallons and gallons of milk each week,

far beyond their nutritional needs. Especially when there are teenagers, a family can find itself forever replenishing its supply. Some older children drink up to a gallon of milk themselves each day. This is an expensive and unnecessary luxury. It may even be detrimental to one's health.

I recently talked with a mother of six teenagers. She complained that her milk bill was extremely high because she continually has to run to the store, almost daily, to replenish the supply for these "hulks" who love to drink milk. Each time her teens pass through the kitchen, they make a milk stop. Allowing this excess gave the mother a milk bill more than twice that which was needful.

It's a matter of the ever-present problem of eating for pleasure rather than for nutrition, a problem afflicting many of us.

You can save tremendously by figuring how much milk nutritionally each person in your family needs. Then buy your milk only once a week and label it for use on certain days. If the limit is exceeded, bring out the powdered milk. Make it do until the next day's allotment.

For one family I know, applying this remedy meant a savings of nearly 50% in their milk bill.

Money Saver Twenty-Three

GET SOFT ON WATER—AND HARD ON CLEANING COSTS!

A water softener can be a real budget booster, helping save on clothes and housework as well as cleaners and soaps.

A well-established water softener company gives the following statistics. The average monthly savings for a family of four using soft water: 65% on laundry soaps and detergents; 100% on chemical water softeners; 50% on bleaches, fabric softeners, dish detergents, hand soaps, lotions and creams, bathsalts and bubble bath; 75% on scouring pads and powder; 15% on clothing and linen; 20% time saved in housework; 25% on plumbing repairs, and other miscellaneous items. These statistics add up to a savings of $6 or $7 per person each month. Of course, our family was not the average family of four. When all eight of our children were living at home, our savings was between $60 and $70 a month or $720 to $840 a year.

With five long-haired daughters and three active sons, there has been a lot of water usage in our home over the past thirty-five plus years, and I can tell you from first-hand experience that this kind of savings was welcomed in our household. The savings allowed us to spend an even greater part of our food budget on the more nutritious and high-quality foods, rather than spending so much money on soaps, shampoos, and cleaners. (The average American family spends around twenty-five percent of their food dollar on non-food items.)

As far as clothing goes, an interesting fact is that items laundered in

soft water will have a 25-30% longer life span. Also the cost of the hot water (electric or gas heated) is 25-30% lower with soft water. Believe me, these savings add up.

We've used a water softener for years. The savings are great! So are soft clothes and soft skin. Soft water dramatically reduces the need for skin lotions and creams. And I can testify to hours and hours of housework saved with no tub or sink rings to scrub. Soft water makes a big difference in all cleaning. A big money saver and a bonus of softer living.

There are other methods of softening water on the market, one of which is magnets being hooked on to your water pipes. Whatever method is used, soft water definitely makes a big difference.

The amount of savings you experience depends, of course, on how hard the water is in your area, the size of your family, and your water usage. For the average family, using some kind of method to soften your water will soon pay for itself.

Money Saver Twenty-Four

TRIMMING THE CHRISTMAS BUDGET

The holidays need not be a hair-raising, hectic,
budget-breaking time if you've planned ahead and
taken advantage of seasonal sales.

I've chosen to discuss Christmas shopping in this book because shopping for Christmas should not be a once-a-year activity. Rather, it's to become part of your shopping plan for the entire year. By planning ahead, you will know your needs for next Christmas. This will allow you to take advantage of seasonal sales as well as avoid the terrible hassle of the last-minute Christmas rush.

You have noticed Christmas decorations in the stores before Halloween. The Christmas holiday consumes our attention for three to four months of the year, and it affects the family budget with similar stress and duration.

We must understand that spending money for Christmas is not ordinary spending. It is sometimes ruthless and abusive because Christmas shopping can be so emotional and contagious. "We can't overlook the Smiths," or "If we give Sally this, we must also give Jenny one so she won't feel left out." Many families spend themselves into debt that lasts for months. They scarcely get on top of one Christmas spending spectacular before the next demanding season is upon them. Therefore, I want to share some helpful tips which will save you money and provide you peace of mind.

Do you approach the Christmas season feeling totally frustrated because your wants in the past have exceeded your pocketbook, causing you to charge and then pay for Christmas for the next six months or so?

Following a few basic suggestions, you'll be able to solve the problem of spending beyond your budget.

First, write down your needs for the year and plan ahead so you can purchase most, if not all, your Christmas items on sale when they're marked down at their lowest. Why not have, for a change, a nice, peaceful Christmas all paid for in advance?

There are certain times when merchants will feature Christmas items on sale. The biggest is the day after Christmas. It's hard for most people to take advantage of day-after-Christmas sales because they've already overspent. If you apply any of the ideas in this hook, DO set aside money each month and put some of those savings into a "Christmas Fund." Make sure you don't dip into this fund for anything other than Christmas. Then, when those fantastic half-price sales come the day after Christmas, you'll have money on hand to take advantage of them.

At the after-Christmas sales you'll find decorations and everything having to do with Christmas marked down drastically—as much as 75-90%. Stores will feature, on the hour, toys, decorations, and other Christmas-related items reduced to practically nothing.

If you spend the morning or afternoon just being in the store, you can pick up very nice dolls and toys for 50-75% off. Many clothing items are also sharply reduced following Christmas so the stores can clear their shelves and make ready for stocking the next season's goods.

There are some stores that will have "Christmas-in-July" sales. Dolls, toys, games, etc. are marked down 25-40%. Many stores also feature Christmas sales in October with equal savings.

Start thinking about next year's Christmas the day after Christmas. You and your budget will be out from under the destructive pressure and you'll enjoy the spirit of the occasion.

Remember...

- Plan ahead.
- Make your lists.
- Establish your Christmas Fund.
- Read the paper daily.

When the opportunity comes, you'll be prepared to take advantage of it. You'll buy quality merchandise for much less and have an enjoyable Christmas knowing you keep your spending within your budget.

And Go!

Money Saver Twenty-Five

ONLY ALONE, AND NEVER WHEN HUNGRY

*Here are two helpful hints for a more economical—and pleasant—
foray into the wilds of the grocery store.*

Shopping on an empty stomach can upset the best shopping plan.
Shopping hungry makes items you otherwise ignore become suddenly
appealing. This is the time you feel like buying candy bars, soda pop,
potato chips—the items you don't really need, budget-wise or health-
wise.

So, remember. Eat something before you leave. Sounds simple? It
is and it's truly a money saver. You'll be able to make a much more
intelligent effort at deciding what you should buy rather than what
looks good to you at the moment.

Leave hubby home, and your children too.

Taking family shopping can be disastrous to your plan for two reasons: With the family along, your attention is continually distracted
from what you're trying to do; that is, shopping wisely and saving
money.

Even if you're armed to the hilt with a list and a definite shopping
strategy, kids will usually start asking and whining for this or that until
you finally give in and buy it for them. It's surprising how all those little extras can add several dollars to your bill, not to mention the fact
that it's hard to keep your mind on what you're doing.

Taking your spouse along can also alter your plans. Spouses are
notoriously impulsive grocery shoppers and often a deterrent to your
shopping plan. They'll likely question your purchases and your plan.
They also like to load unbudgeted "yummies" into the cart that are on

neither your menus nor your list.

Remember, taking family members to the store can be a threat to your food budget. Your savings from wise shopping will more than compensate for babysitting expenses.

Leave the darlings home!
Shopping is strictly business
...and survival in today's economy.
They'll understand.
And you will all be richer!

Money Saver Twenty-Six

GENERALLY GENERIC OR BRILLIANTLY BRANDED?

Name brand or no-name? The choice is yours—
and so are the savings!

The term "generic" refers to products with labels having no name brand, only an identification of the product. With canned goods, the can will be wrapped in white paper and have "Pears" written on it.

Often, the only difference between no-name and name-brand cans is that content size may vary or there may have been a mar in the fruit or vegetable, similar to seconds in clothing. Many times canneries will run one brand's label and as soon as they're finished, they'll continue the same product with another label.

I suggest when you buy generic goods, you sample a can before buying the whole case to make sure you're getting the quality you wish. Try different generic products. You may find some acceptable to you and your family.

"House-brand" products can also be big money savers. These are goods on which the grocery store chain puts its own label. Because the chain may have several stores throughout a region, it often sells these goods at a lower cost—even though the quality may be as good as higher brand merchandise. I recommend you become familiar with house brands. The savings are often considerable, especially during store promotions and case lot sales.

Experiment. Test both the generic and house-brand products.

Money Saver Twenty-Seven

IS BIGGER BETTER? BUYING IN BULK

Savings can be big in bulk; if you can't use it all,
split with a neighbor.

For the large family, buying in bulk is cost and time effective. For instance, for our family of ten to buy beans, rice or flour in a small package, less than ten pounds, would be an inefficient use of time and money. Usually you have to pay more per pound and more frequently replenish your supply with smaller sizes.

Let's say your family loves chile con carne and Mexican foods and so eats large amounts of pinto beans. In your case, you should buy them in the 25 pound or even 50 or 100 pound bag. Prices fluctuate, but within the past year I could buy 100 pounds of pintos for $45.70. I found that if I had purchased 100 pounds in four-pound packages selling at $2.59 each, in a local grocery store, I would have paid 65 cents a pound or $65.00 per 100 lbs. Buying the beans at the same store in a "scoop your own" bin would cost 79 cents a pound or $79.00 per one hundred pounds. Buying in larger quantities at a wholesale grain business for $45.70, saved me $33.00, a 58% savings.

The savings may have been even more because over the several months of consumption the price on the smaller packages (and bulk) would likely have increased. Purchasing the 100 lbs. is a single expense with a fixed price.

A year ago I purchased 100 pounds of pinto beans and paid $45.70. That bulk price itself may have increased since that time, depending upon the weather which may affect the crop and the price, and depending upon which business I buy the beans from.

Speaking of pinto beans, I made an interesting observation one day while in a grocery store. They were featuring basics—beans, flour, rice, etc. Twenty-five pound bags of pintos were selling for $17.95 or $71.80 per hundred. In their "bulk" section where you scoop your own, pintos were 79 cents a pound, or $79.00 per hundred. In yet another location, pintos were in four-pound packages selling at $2.59 or $64.75 per hundred.

Interesting, isn't it? In the same store, three different prices on the same pinto beans.

Cost per...		*bag*	*pound*	*100 lbs.*
Store A				
Location 1	25 lb. bag	$17.95	$.71	$71.88
Location 2	scoop bulk		.79	79.00
Location 3	4 lb. bag	2.59	.65	65.00
Store B	100 lb. bag		.457	45.70
Savings				33.30

Notice that their "bulk" (a term understood by customers to mean savings) was not the cheapest. It was the most expensive. So beware. Bulk buying in this store is not a savings at all. We expect it to be, but too often stores take advantage of us in ways that can be misleading and expensive.

Rice is another good example of savings with a higher poundage purchase. Within the past year a high quality, name-brand white rice sold for $3.69 a five-pound bag. I could buy 100 pounds of the same quality for $33.00 compared to $73.80 for 100 pounds of the small bags. Buying the larger bags (2-50#) saved me $40.80, a 55% savings. I would be able to buy more than twice the rice. If rice or beans or any other such items are products you use, consider buying enough for a year or two. Of course, proper storage would be a must. By doing this, you save not only a large amount of money but a great deal of time and effort in the purchasing of the items.

Many grocery stores feature "bulk" buying sections, displaying scores of the bulk foodstuffs in barrels or other attractive containers and allowing customers to scoop their own. The idea they want to put across is that this is bulk and therefore much cheaper. Occasionally it may be, but in my experience these "bulk" prices are without exception higher than the packaged items on the shelf.

Deceptive, isn't it. You can see the need to be "shopper smart."

Another caution with open bulk is sanitation. Allowing everyone, including children, to put their hands into the container to scoop raises a question of cleanliness. If price is not an advantage, I prefer the sanitary protection of packages.

I am familiar with a local store specializing in nothing but bulk where temperatures are kept cool to minimize infestation. I am frequently able to obtain many things here which are not always available elsewhere. This is a convenience, but not a savings. So again I say, do not let the term "bulk buying" lead you to think cheaper without some investigation. The truly bargain bulk buying, in my experience, is found at grain outlets and mills. It's here where you can get the basics, packaged and at much lower prices than at retail stores.

Beans and other legumes, like grains, store well if kept in airtight containers in a cool, dry area. Purchasing 100 lbs. once a year provides all you need and saves you money as well.

Smaller families can benefit from bulk buying too. Friends, neighbors, and relatives are happy to share the 100 lbs. with you, allowing all to reap the savings. I've never met anyone yet who didn't appreciate getting in on a good deal saving money.

A good idea when buying bulk is to consider all the alternatives to determine whether savings are available or not. Sometimes the savings just aren't there. Leader specials on small sized packages may offer a better savings than bulk. There are times when bulk prices rise because of shortages.

Never assume there is only one way to do your shopping. Weigh all possibilities; consider all angles. And don't think you have to run from store to store to check out the information. The yellow pages and telephone will save you hours of time, leg work, gas expense, and energy.

Also use the yellow pages to locate outlets for grain in bulk—flour mills, co-ops, and stores selling bulk. Health food stores carry some bulk items. If a store doesn't sell bulk retail, ask them to order 50 or 100 lbs. for you for a small fee. I've done this many times. Health stores usually buy their grains in bulk and break them down to sell in smaller packages at higher prices. Ask them to sell bulk to you for that extra fee, then arrange with your friends to split with you. You both win with your savings and the store makes a worthwhile profit.

If you have no local bulk outlets, check neighboring towns. In a small town 15 minutes drive from my home is a rolling mill that not only sells grains in bulk, but will mill it into flour as well. This allows me convenient access to big savings plus fresh, nutritious, ground flour.

If you don't have a grinder, consider buying freshly-milled flour from a roller mill. However you "stack it," bulk usually offers big savings.

Money Saver Twenty-Eight
S-T-R-E-T-C-H-I-N-G THE FOOD DOLLAR—
A CASE IN POINT

Start your storage by buying just one case a month, and plan ahead for the case lot sales.

An excellent way to get ahead of weekly and monthly buying is to purchase items by the case. There are months of the year when certain foods will almost always be on sale. By knowing when those occur and planning ahead, you'll be able to save hundreds of dollars.

To wit: many case lot sales occur during August and September when certain fruits and vegetables are plentiful. The stores will mark down these canned items and sell them either by the can, by the half case, or by the whole case.

There are times when frozen goods will be marked down at the grocery store. Try getting into the habit of waiting to buy these items until they're on sale. Then, instead of buying two or three single units, buy a case or two, depending on how much you'll use during the year. A well-known brand of orange juice sells for 50 cents a can during an annual sale and later sells for $1.09. Why pay the extra 59 cents?

It means a savings of $14.16 buying on sale by the case—a 55% savings.

Paper items, as almost everything in a grocery store, will be on sale some time or other during the year. Try planning into your system the buying of these items by the case, too. Let me explain. A certain expensive name brand of toilet paper went on sale for $1.99 a four-roll pack. The original price was $2.89 a pack. By purchasing a case of 24 on sale, I saved $21.60—a 68% savings.

The main reason people don't buy case lots is lack of money. When you're on a tight food budget, there just never seems to be enough money to buy cases. Believe me, there is if you will follow this simple plan:

Make a running list of cases of food you'd like to have in your food storage. Then, before you buy your other items for the month, select at least one of these items and purchase a case. (You do this, of course, after you've read the newspaper ads and found out what is on sale or what is a leader.)

There are many cases of food which you can buy for $10 or less. By purchasing even one case a month (and more as your savings add up), you'll soon find your storage shelves filling up and surplus items left over from the previous month's shopping will continue to increase.

Implementing just this one practice into your shopping habits will save you hundreds of dollars each year. Get in the habit of checking case prices and start buying by the case, and saving by the case.

Remember the plan...

- Make a list of cases of food you want to store.
- Watch for sales.
- On your shopping trip buy that case first—before anything else.
- Do it each month (at least one case a month).

Money Saver Twenty-Nine

INSTITUTIONAL SIZES AREN'T JUST FOR SCHOOLS AND HOSPITALS

Families can use them, too. Purchase this extra-large size and realize large size savings.

Institutional-size items are those packed in large quantities sold to institutions such as hospitals, restaurants, rest homes, and schools. More and more stores are now selling them to the public. Check the yellow pages to see if there are businesses in your town which deal only in institutional sizes. They'll often sell to individuals as well as institutions.

Think about it. you can probably use larger cans of such items as fruits, mayonnaise, chow mein noodles, just to mention a few. Putting the extra in your fridge (to be used within a safe period of time) or into tightly-sealed bottles in your pantry for future use, will enable you to save money.

I've been able to buy large twelve pound boxes of nacho chips for $12. At the store I would pay $2.44 for a one pound package of the same quality. This represents a $1.44 per pound savings of 59%.

No need to pass up savings through large quantity purchases. If you think your family cannot use all the contents before it wastes, call a friend and share. Any one of my neighbors would be willing to take advantage of a half-price savings.

Money Saver Thirty

FARMERS AREN'T THE ONLY ONES WITH A CO-OP

It may mean having to organize it yourself, but belonging to a co-op can mean great savings for your food budget.

Co-op means, of course, cooperation. If several interested peo-ple—neighbors, relatives or friends—get together to form a group for the purpose of buying food products, the savings can be substantial.

We belonged to such a group, and we found the buying power brings prices down considerably. A co-op operates without profit and therefore is tax free—constituting a double savings. To belong, each person is required to do a little work each month, which is the under-lying principle of a co-op. Each pitches in with the work and saves that amount otherwise paid in wages.

Because of the large membership, a co-op has significant buying power—clout—that opens accounts with wholesale distributors. For truck-load orders these companies will cut their prices even further.

For instance, when sugar was selling for $34 a 100 lbs., our co-op, by ordering a semi-truck load, was able to get sugar at $26 a 100 lbs., a 24% savings, which makes 'co-oping' worthwhile for me.

The co-op I belonged to regularly ordered quality cheese from the factory. By purchasing five-pound bricks, or 13 lb. horns, we saved $1.33 per lb. It retailed at $2.98 a lb. or $38.74 for the 13 lbs. I paid the co-op price of $1.65 per lb. or $21.45 for the 13 lb. horn, a savings of $17.39 or 45%. Mind you, this is cheese of superior quality—the best. So you see, a co-op affords us the best at considerable savings. And that is worth a one or two hour assignment now and again.

Another benefit of co-op is the "endless" variety of food selection. Our co-op surveyed the wishes of its members when making up an order. The co-op also offered grains in bulk—100 lb. bags, institution-al-size items, certain meats, canned goods, spices, just about anything we needed for our family.

Following is an example of how a neighborhood co-op might be organized; the pattern, rules and guidelines being simplified suggestions only.

In establishing a co-op, you may structure it as simple or as elaborate as co-op members desire. In our example you can see there are three levels of administration—neighborhood group, district and general. The neighborhood group is the basic unit. It is comprised of six to eight households or members living within close proximity.

As your co-op membership increases the organization may expand to include several of the basic groups requiring the creation of a district level to supervise the total operation.

Greater expansion requires a third or general level, the officers of which oversee several districts which in turn oversee their basic neighborhood groups. General level leadership promotes the proper and efficient functioning of the entire co-op at all levels.

Co-ops are a popular means of cutting costs throughout the country. They range in size from the small neighborhood group we've been discussing to storefront cooperatives, co-op supermarkets and even multi-state warehousing cooperatives.

From my experience I have observed that growth in size of co-ops is beneficial. However, there seems to be an undeterminable peak of growth after which is evident a diminishing of returns—too big for maximum benefits in savings and effort.

The key to any co-op regardless of size of membership or levels of  organization is commitment and responsibility—commitment to the primary goal of big savings for everyone, being responsible for adherence to rules and guidelines, and punctually fulfilling assignments and performing the work required of each co-op member.

Co-op means cooperation, everyone carrying their fair load and mutually benefiting in big savings.

Neighborhood Cooperative Organization Chart

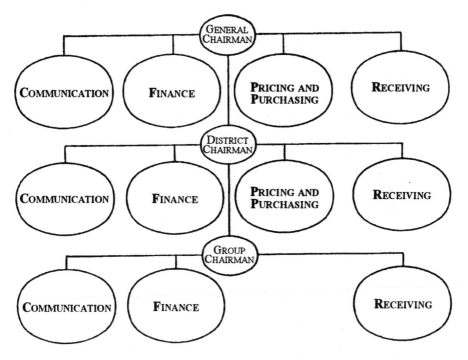

Co-op Rules

1. Application Form and Membership Contract Agreement to be signed in duplicate and submitted with fees to Chairperson. Notice of approval or denial will be given within seven working days. In event of application denial, fees will be refunded with accompanying reasons for denial of membership given in writing at time of notice.
2. Initial membership fee of $2.00 per member.
3. Monthly fee of $1.00 per member. Monthly fee will be paid prior to each six-month period—January and July. Members joining within a period will pay a prorated amount for remaining months, plus the initial fee. Delinquent fees are cause for forfeiture of membership after 30 days.
4. Orders will be submitted to Finance Chairperson by date and

within hours designated on order form.

5. Order payment, cash or check (NO two-party checks allowed) accompanies all orders. A $10.00 service charge levied on each returned check.

6. Errors, problems, questions are to be resolved on lowest level possible. Each member is responsible for own errors.

7. Product pick-up during designated hours on assigned day only. In case of emergency-exceptions, contact will be made with Receiving Chairperson. Orders not picked up within 48 hours will be sold without reimbursement. Punctual pick-up is vital to co-op success.

8. Back orders will be given credit on next order. No refunds. The Receiving Chairperson is required to notify the Backorder Chairperson of all backorders by 9:30 p.m. on pick-up day.

9. Delivered goods must be accepted by members, except in event of spoilage, damage, unacceptable quality, etc., in which event recourse—credit or replacement—is arranged with Receiving Chairperson within seven working days of receipt and with contents and original packaging. No refunds.

10. Cooperative effort is required from each member. Failure to fulfill assigned responsibilities is cause for forfeiture of membership. Exceptions allowed when responsible substitution arranged and satisfactorily completed.

11. Cause for forfeiture of membership:
    a. Delinquency of fines or fee payments beyond 30 day grace period.
    b. Refusal to abide by Co-op rules and regulations.
    c. Unsatisfactory completion of co-op assignments and duties.
    d. Unwarranted harassment of officers, business contacts or others fulfilling assignments.
    e. Unsatisfactory conduct which undermines co-op goals and functions.

12. Reporting of good buys to Purchasing Committee is urged of all members.

Money Saver Thirty-One

TO MARKET, TO MARKET

Discover a whole new world of unbelievable buys
at the farmers market.

A farmer's market is a distribution center of fresh produce found in most, if not all, large cities. It may consist of several buildings, each owned and operated separately by different parties. Each market receives truck loads of produce from farming regions both in and out of state. Here, local grocers come to replenish their retail grocery supplies.

And this is where you'll come, too, once you've decided to take advantage of all the great things awaiting you at the farmers' market. But don't come alone. Bring two or three friends or neighbors. This means greater purchasing power by pooling your shopping monies. It also means being able to share in produce, not to mention the fun and friendship. Your group will want to have a pickup truck, camper, station wagon or van so you'll have room to haul your produce.

Naturally the retail grocers want their shelves stocked and ready when their stores open each day. For that reason the farmers' market operation takes place very early in the morning. That's why your excursion to the market must also begin very early, even before the proverbial cock crows—perhaps even 4 or 5 a.m. Then you'll be there just as the luscious fresh produce comes off the trucks, and before the retail grocers have it picked over. You'll be ecstatic over how beautiful it is.

Here the produce is only a day or two from the field. It hasn't been pinched, bruised or dropped by scores of people. Once you've experienced the farmers' market, I guarantee you'll never be content to go back to the frustration and frenzy of ordinary shopping.

Now these farmers' markets may be right in your city, or they may be some distance away, taking an hour or so to get there. It doesn't matter. You're with friends who share common interests and have much to talk about. It's a lark. It's fun. It's money in your pocket. And it's an absolutely charming way to break the monotony of everyday routine. You'll love it.

Have your produce list prepared in advance. Take a clip board and calculator along.

When you arrive look up the manager. Tell him you represent a buyer's group wanting case prices on the produce you are interested in. Give him your group name (one you've already selected). Because you represent big-dollar volume, most of these mangers will show an interest in doing business and will quote you their case lot prices. Some may not.

It's important that you stay in command of the situation. Don't feel shy or intimidated. Don't be afraid to shop around and compare prices and quality. Take notes on the different items you're interested in and write down the prices. Do this in several of the markets. In most cities the markets are all in the same complex, all within walking distance, usually next door to each other. So you go from building to building taking notes and making comparisons.

By this time, you'll start feeling as if you've discovered a gold mine, a bonanza! So now is the time to exercise some restraint. Beforehand you'll have decided how much of a particular item you want; that is, one case between you, two cases, or three. You must buy in case lots, but you may split that case in halves, thirds, fourths, or whatever the group determines. (Do the actual dividing after you leave.)

You won't necessarily buy all items at the same building. You pay cash. Most marketers have the cases ready on the dock and will load them in the van.

All these details you'll learn as you frequent the market and get to know the marketers. You'll find that after they've seen you a few times, they'll become increasingly accommodating and helpful because they know you're serious customers.

So you make your purchases, load up and head for home.

When you arrive home everything is in crates, lugs and boxes. You may want to unload your cargo in the garage of the group member who's most centrally located. After unloading, you'll divide the produce according to your pre-arranged lists. It shouldn't take long.

Your family is just awakening and will not have missed you. When they see what you've brought home, they'll "oooh" and "aaah" just as you did. In their excitement they'll want to taste this and that. That's good, but enough is enough! Before they "spoil the pudding and go off to their different activities, put them to work carrying and storing. This way it becomes a family affair and a simple, fun task for all.

Obviously, buying in bulk this way requires some extra space to store your produce until needed. A second refrigerator is ideal for storing your produce and preserving its freshness until it's ready to use.

A tip on storing. Do not wash the produce until ready to use. Place in plastic bags and tie, making it as air-tight as possible. This will keep the produce fresh for three to four weeks.

With cool weather, a corner of your garage, pantry or basement room will serve for the storage of some of your produce—apples, oranges, etc. Of course, the most ideal storage would be the second refrigerator. Three or four trips to the farmers' market will save you enough for the purchase of that second refrigerator.

Just how much were you able to save by taking this trip to the market? To put it mildly, you've made a killing with savings of over 50%—meaning that for every dollar you have in your food budget, you still have more than 50¢ left! To illustrate the savings, I've included the following chart of one of my trips to the farmers' market. There were three of us. We spent a total of $148 which would have cost us $313.83 at the grocery store. We saved $165.83—a 53% savings. This means I fed my family of 10 all the fresh fruits and vegetables they could eat for a little more than $2.00 a day.

And just what else have you accomplished with this trip to the farmers' market besides big savings? Well, you have the freshest, best quality fruits and vegetables possible outside of being a farmer and growing them yourself. You have a variety not before enjoyed by you and your family, which means better nutrition. And you've had an enjoyable time with your friends. What more could you ask?

Shopping At Farmers' Market Vs. Local Grocery Store

Item	#	Case Price	Amt	Farmers' Market	Grocery Store	Group Savings	My Savings*
Avocados	1 @	$10.00	40	$10.00	$13.00	$3.00	$1.50
Broccoli	1 @	7.50	23#	7.50	15.18	7.68	2.56
Celery	1 @	7.50	24	7.50	17.22	10.22	4.40
Grapefruit	2 @	8.00	32	16.00	38.40	22.40	11.20
Grapes (Gr)	1 @	17.50	23#	17.50	45.54	28.04	14.02
Grapes (Rd)	1 @	9.50	23#	9.50	18.17	8.67	4.43
Lemons	1 @	7.50	95	7.50	24.00	16.50	5.50
Lettuce	1 @	6.50	24	6.50	24.96	18.46	9.23
Mushrooms	1 @	9.00	11#	9.00	26.29	17.29	5.76
Onions (Rd)	1 @	8.00	25#	8.00	22.25	14.25	4.75
Oranges	4 @	5.75	88	23.00	29.80	6.80	1.74
Pineapple	1 @	11.00	8	11.00	13.52	2.52	.84
Tomatoes	1 @	15.00	50	15.00	25.00	10.00	3.33
Totals				$148.00	$313.83	$165.83 (53%)	$69.26 (53%)

*Some of the cases were split in 1/3's and some in ½'s.

This trip was taken in early spring by three women. After shopping at the farmers' market, a comparison shopping trip was made to two local grocery stores on that same day. The top price was used in this study. These would be the prices which would have been paid if the women had shopped locally.

Reasons why it pays to shop at farmers' market...

1. Money Savings. ($165.83 for the three women—a 53% savings. My savings was $69.26.)
2. Better Nutrition. (You and your family can eat all the fresh fruits and vegetables you wish instead of limiting yourselves.)
3. Better quality and much fresher produce. (Because much of the produce arrives at the beginning of the week, you know it has not been sitting for a long time.)

To market . . . to market
with friends, bright and early,
and home again in a van
loaded with lush fruits & vegetables
at unbelievable savings.

THE FARMER IN THE DELL—OR—
IN YOUR OWN NEIGHBORHOOD

*Bushels and boxes and lugs of fresh fruit and vegetables
are closer than you think—and for a lot less.*

A local apple grower told me that purchasing apples by the pound causes you to end up paying more than $25 per bushel. Why do that when you can buy directly from the apple grower himself and pay only $8 to $10 a bushel? The same goes for cherries, peaches, potatoes, onions, squash—any kind of fruit or vegetable that's in season.

Our family devours huge quantities of fresh fruits and vegetables. This pleases me because I've found it's a great way to maximize nutrition in the diet. And buying from the farmer is a great way to put money in my pocket!

In Money Saver Fourteen we discussed the preservation of fruits and vegetables. Buying direct from the farmer makes food preservation very inexpensive. Compare for yourself. Price canned fruits and vegetables at your local grocery store. Then check the farmers' column or the fruits and vegetable section of your newspaper and see what those items are selling for by the bushel, case or lug when in season. You've paid a low price (on sale) for your sugar and canning jars, and now you can save many times over by buying direct from the farmer and canning your own fruits and vegetables.

Buying from the farmer you also save the fruit stand mark-up as well as the higher mark-up at the grocery store. You will save even more by taking family members with you and picking your own fruits and vegetables. Anything you can do yourself saves you money because each time a product is handled, the price goes up. When you finally buy it at the store, the mark-up is almost doubled!

Buying direct from the farmer depends, of course, on where you live—whether you're close to farms and fields. Your savings make even a one or two hour drive worthwhile. Make it a family outing. Buying direct from the farmer can be fun for the whole family. Take the kids along. Let them see a real farm and learn that food doesn't grow on grocers' shelves. Have your children participate in selecting your purchases. It will create in them greater interest in meals, proper nutrition and wise use of money.

If you're unaware of farms and orchards close by, check the classified section of the newspaper, or ask your grocer where he gets his produce, if there are local farmers. They are out there. Take a pleasure drive out into the country, and ask. You'll find them. Happy picking!

Money Saver Thirty-Three

CAN'T STAND IT? TRY FRESH FRU VEGETABLES

If buying direct from the farmer is not possible or convenient, try the next best thing: a produce stand.

In our area, there are fields and orchards close by, and during the summer months numerous little product stands open up for the sale of fresh fruits and vegetables. Fruit stand prices, although a little higher than buying direct from the farmer, are lower than you'd pay at the grocery stores. For small or large quantities, fruit stands are a good way to put fresh fruits and vegetables on your table at a low cost.

Some of the stands remain open year round, keeping their produce in cold storage. Thus, I'm able to feed my family fresh produce during the winter months. These fresh, delicious fruits and vegetables are a welcome addition to the lunches we make at home.

I've been able to buy 50 pounds of onions (which will last through the winter, with proper storage) for as low as $5 or $6 a bag. During the winter when the price of onions climbs to 60-70 cents a pound, I haven't had to pay $35.00 for that 50 pounds—a savings of over 80%.

Over a period of months, the savings keep growing. Instead of buying apples by the pound (they can get as high as 99 cents a pound in grocery stores), I can purchase a box of apples from fruit stand cold storage for $8 to $10 a box, depending upon the quality and size—another possible savings of $27.62 or 75%.

Money Saver Eleven—a second refrigerator—allows you to make this method of shopping and savings very effective and convenient.

Money Saver Thirty-Four

THE INCONVENIENT COST OF CONVENIENCE FOODS

You'd be surprised at the price you pay for convenience.
Why not make your own?

Any time you buy such items as TV dinners, frozen pizzas, frozen pies or cakes or cookie dough, you pay a high price for convenience. Do a study of the convenience foods you buy—frequency and cost. You might decide that you are paying more than it's worth for the convenience.

These items in the frozen foods section of the store were selling at the following prices:

Four breaded chicken patties (12 oz.)	$2.51
Chopped sirloin beef dinner (12 oz.)	2.69
Apple pie (1 lb. 10 oz.)	1.97
Three loaves frozen bread dough (3 lbs.)	1.63
Eight waffles (8 oz.)	.95
Six pizza rolls (6 oz.)	1.05

At first glance, the prices don't look so bad. But let's figure it out: 12 ounces of chicken patties for $2.51 means you're paying $3.35 per pound! Chicken patties can easily be made with chicken bought on sale, sometimes for as little as 49¢ a pound. Compare the difference— a gigantic 85% savings. Remember that you're paying not just for the chicken in the patties, but for the breaded part as well.

The 12-ounce chopped sirloin dinner had only a few green beans and a spoonful of mashed potatoes with a little gravy on top. Homemade frozen dinners like that could be put together for less than half the price.

Waffles. Why not make your own and freeze a few to pop in the toaster when you're in a hurry? The above listed price is $1.90 a pound.

As for the frozen apple pie, it would cost less than a dollar to buy apples by the bushel and flour by the 50 or 100 lb. sack to make it. And "your" pie will taste better, too!

Buying frozen bread dough is admittedly cheaper than buying loaves of bread, but making your own for about 25 cents a loaf is even better.

With a little planning and scheduling you can make your own convenience foods and not be inconvenienced. It doesn't take as long as you might think.

If your family enjoys a quick TV dinner or frozen pizza now and then, why not spend an hour or two occasionally making your own "quickies" to freeze for later use? (Incidentally, did you know that most frozen pizzas are not made with real cheese, but with an artificial substitute?) Then when you want that TV dinner or pizza, at the 'snap of a finger,' run to the freezer, not the grocery store. Warm it in the oven and presto, "Quick as a wink"—your convenience dinner, without the inconvenience of high price. The nutritional value and tastiness will be greatly improved over those instant dinners you have purchased at the store.

Money Saver Thirty-Five

JUNK THE JUNK FOOD

$100 a year for candy bars? $146 for soft drinks?
By eliminating soda pop, candy, potato chips, and other
junk foods your health and budget benefits will be enormous.

The adage "an apple a day will keep the doctor away" may well have been replaced by the practice of indulging ourselves with a daily candy bar and soft drink. This is the habit of many, many Americans, yes, and peoples throughout the world.

Consider the costs: Candy bars at 30¢. One a day for 365 a year-$109.50. Soft drinks, 40¢ each. Taken daily, 365 days—$146. That's one person. Consider the cost for a family. WOW! Is the luxury worth it? Have you ever considered cutting junk food out of your food budget? We have made the attempt, and we've found the difference to be amazing.

Assuming you buy a few candy bars when you go to the store, let's figure six candy bars at 30¢ each. You'd pay $1.80. That doesn't sound like much, but if you do this each time you shop, and you shop once a week, you're spending $93.60 each year on candy bars alone! Think of it—cutting candy bars out of your grocery shopping will save you $93.60 and you'll be better off health-wise, too.

Potato chips. If you buy a bag a week at $1.50 (minimal) you'll pay $78 a year for potato chips. Nutritionally, potato chips are way down the list. They are high in salt and fats. The less you have of these in your diet, the better, according to the National Academy of Sciences' anti-cancer diet.

Soft drinks, too, can hurt the budget and the body. It's the great American drink-but you'd be better off without it. When all eight of our children were home, if we were the "average" soda pop drinking family, we could have spent $1,460 a year on soda pop alone. Think what it could have done to our budget, not to mention our health. With all the caffeine, sugar, saccharine, nutra-sweet and carbonation, soda pop is hard on our systems. One urologist said he would be out of business if people stopped drinking soda pop.

Ice cream is a great American past time. But it can also be a great part of the American food budget. The average family spends around $600 a year on ice cream, frozen yogurts, frozen pops, etc.

Eliminating just the four items we've discussed here, a family's yearly food savings could easily be $2,231.60. If this is you, isn't there something else you'd rather do with over $2000? Could you cut the spending back at least half that much and go easy on these unnecessary items?

Compute the costs of enjoying other junk foods that make up your eating habits. Potato chips, gum, ice cream, tobacco, alcoholic beverages—whatever is short on nutrition and long on possible bodily harm. Again I ask, is the cost worth the luxury? Is it unrealistic to pretend to do away with candy, gum, soft drinks, and potato chips? Probably. Minimizing the consumption of junk foods would have to be considered a victory.

Try these compromises. Make a deal with your family after teaching them the nutritional and budgetary advantages for cutting down on junk foods. The deal is this: a "blow day." All the family conscientiously retrains from junk food for several days. Then comes the reward-blow day," a special day, an outing, trip or picnic when the family blows it—casts the restrictions aside and eats junk food.

Another idea is to purge your fridge and menus, but serve the junk food on special occasions—Sunday dinner, birthday parties and dinners, picnics, eating out, etc.

These and other compromises will go a long way in helping your family minimize junk food intake and improve their health (and your pocketbook).

Money Saver Thirty-Six

CEREAL SAGA

Consider the cost and health benefits of taking boxed cereals off your grocery list and making your own.

If you go to the grocery store and price boxed cereals, you'll find that it is difficult to buy any brand for less than $2.50. On a recent shopping trip, I priced ten name-brand cold cereals as follows:

Brand A (14 oz.)	3.49	(3.72 per lb.)
Brand B (1 lb. 4 oz.)	3.85	(3.08 per lb.)
Brand C (1 lb. 3.7 oz.)	3.92	(3.59 per lb.)
Brand D (2 lbs.)	4.15	(2.08 per lb.)
Brand E (1 lb. 8.5 oz.)	4.65	(3.04 per lb.)
Brand F (1 lb. 8 oz.)	2.39	(1.59 per lb.)
Brand G (1 lb. 1.5 oz.)	4.09	(3.64 per lb.)
Brand H (1 lb. 4 oz.)	4.29	(3.43 per lb.)
Brand I (6 oz.)	1.99	(4.55 per lb.)
Brand J (1 lb. 1.5 oz.)	3.29	(3.01 per lb.)

This averaged out to $3.61 per box or $3.17 per lb.

For a large family, one box hardly lasts one breakfast meal, two at the most. Some families also used boxed cereals for suppers. The tendency is to eat several servings because cold cereal isn't very filling But it's fun...and easy...and quick.

If my family were to eat only cold cereals for breakfast for one week, I would probably need to purchase at least seven boxes That would cost me $25 a week or $108 a month or $1300 a year. You can see that a great deal of one's food budget could go into cold cereals alone.

Let's compare this with using the whole grains (ground or blended in a blender). If I were to grind 1¼ c. of wheat into cereal form and cook it in the top of a double boiler, I could serve my family of ten for about 25 cents for just the cereal. Comparing this to $2-$4 for one morning's boxed cereal means at least an 80% savings. In addition, the nutritional value of the breakfast is greatly improved with the whole grain which provides the vitamins and minerals which are left out of the heavily processed boxed cereals.

If I were to buy 100 pounds of Brand A cereal over a year's time, I would spend $372, or $308 for Brand B, $359 for Brand C, and $455 for Brand I. One hundred pounds of rolled oats would cost me around $32. By comparing whole grain cereals vs. boxed cereals, we find much money goes into the refining and packaging of the boxed cereals. It is a little known fact that the packaging of boxed cereals costs 150% more than the value of the food itself. Let's talk about some fiber-rich, whole-grain cereals. By going to a nearby roller mill, I can buy the following: 100 lb. Turkey Red, high protein, low moisture wheat $16.40 (2-50 lb. bags @ $8.20), 50 lb. unbleached flour $7.55, 25 lb. germade (Cream-of-Wheat-like cereal) $5.97, 10 lb. table bran $4.70, and 5 lb. wheat germ $3.45. With tax at $2.37, the total bill for 190 lb. of nutrition would be $40.45, an average of 21¢ a pound.

This $40.45 whole grain and fiber-rich food investment will last my family for 8 to 10 months and will allow me to put superior nutrition into a great variety of dishes—hot and cold cereals, granola, pancakes, waffles, muffins, breads, rolls, cakes, cookies, pies, pizzas, puddings, casseroles, etc. By spending $40 on the "usuals" at the grocery store, I would come home with one or two sacks of food items which last my family for a week or less. Compare: 100 lbs. wheat at $16.40 with 11 loaves of 100% whole wheat bread at $1.49 or $16.39 total. Think of the many dozens of loaves of bread and goodies you could make with that 100 pounds of wheat, not to mention the many servings of breakfast cereal you could serve your family, thus stretching that food dollar into months of use, while the eleven loaves of bread would be gone in a matter of days.

Other whole grains which make tasty cereals are rice, oats, germade (made from wheat) and corn. Make your own granola. It is so good and far superior to store brands, and much, much less expensive.

Samples of breakfast for the week could be: cracked whole wheat, ground whole grain rice (which cooks up similar to cream of wheat), germade, oatmeal cereal, granola, whole wheat pancakes, and whole wheat waffles.

Whole grains are nutritionally high in vitamins and minerals as well as protein. By the time you add fruit and milk to the meal, you have a nutritional breakfast spending far less than with boxed cereals or the traditional ham, bacon or sausage and egg and toast breakfast. You'll also find that your breakfast stays with you longer and you'll not get those 11 o'clock hunger pangs.

Money Saver Thirty-Seven

"Day Old" Is Not Too Old— And It's A Lot Cheaper!

If you're not into breadmaking, consider buying day-old bread and rolls at the bakery or thrift store.

In most localities there are "day-old bakeries" or thrift stores where you can purchase bread that's just been taken off the shelves at the grocery stores. Stores remove it in order to keep their shelves stocked with "fresh" appealing bakery goods. This bread isn't stale. It's usually not more than one or two days old.

The cost of this bread, however, is cut anywhere from one-third to one-half. For instance, whole wheat bread which averages $1.25 per loaf in the grocery stores can be purchased at the day-old bakery for about $1.60 for two loaves—a savings of 90¢ (36%) on the purchase of two loaves.

If you have invested in a freezer, you may want to purchase a large supply of day-old bread and freeze it. This way you'll have plenty of bread on hand and so eliminate those unnecessary trips to the store.

The thrift stores and day-old bakeries also carry pastries, cookies, donuts, cupcakes, etc., all selling for less than you'd normally pay. Try patronizing "day-old" stores and see if you're not amazed at what you save by making this part of your shopping routine. It's the next best thing to making your own breadstuffs.

Often we find ourselves running to the grocery store for a loaf of bread for lunches or a gallon of milk for breakfast. But is that all we buy, or do we pick up a "few" extra things in addition to the bread and/or milk? When we do this, our loaf of bread or gallon of milk can cost us $25 a trip. Four of those trips a month can cause us to throw away $100 of our food budget and we can't account for much else than four loaves of bread or four gallons of milk. (see Money Saver Twenty-Two).

Buying bread at a thrift store once a month and freezing the products will save a great deal of our time and money and cut out some of those "quick" trips to the grocery store. We will use our "home store" instead of the grocery store. If you are interested in saving considerably more money, make your own bread at 25 cents a loaf.

Money Saver Thirty-Eight

CHEAPER BY THE FLAT: EGG-ZACTLY THE RIGHT PRICE

*Where does your grocer buy eggs? Maybe you can buy
them there, too, and save a nest full. Every Henny Penny counts!*

Where do grocers buy their eggs? You may want to ask around or check the yellow pages to see if there's an egg distributor in your area. We have one that is a 10-minute drive from home, and it's a big money saver.

By hopping into the car and making one visit a month, I can buy several flats of jumbo, extra large, or large Grade A eggs which are more fresh and less expensive. I can buy several flats of jumbo Grade A eggs for $1.45 per flat (20 eggs). That compares to $1.09 per dozen at the local grocery store. The flat averages a little over 7 cents per egg. The grocery-store dozen averages a little over 9 cents per egg. That is a savings of 2 cents per egg or 33% savings.

It should be noted here that the price of eggs varies from month to month depending upon factors affecting the production of eggs. The above figures are actual costs of eggs during a given month.

To see what your savings could be, figure out how many eggs your family eats each week and how much you usually pay per dozen. The savings per egg may not seem like much until you remember that every penny counts, especially when you consider the cost over a year's time. You may decide that it's very much worth your while to start buying your eggs by the flat (or even

by the half or full case) at the egg plant.

Buying chex or "B's" is another way of increasing these savings. Chex eggs are those with cracks and can be used for baking. It is a fact that professional bakers do buy these eggs already frozen and use them in their breads and baked products. At the present time, I would hesitate using them in my baking because of the salmonella factor. "B's" are those eggs which have odd shapes and do not look like the regular shape egg. Usually the chex or "B's" have to be special ordered.

If you've invested in a second refrigerator, you could buy your eggs in bulk by the half or whole case. Eggs store for a long time in the fridge without spoiling. This does away with having to run to the store for eggs every week, eliminating that trip saves you money and time .

If you don't have space in your fridge for that many eggs, consider splitting your purchase with a neighbor and letting her enjoy the savings, too.

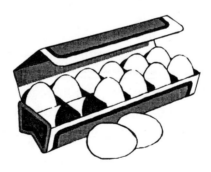

Money Saver Thirty-Nine

BABY + HOME-PREPARED FOOD: A GOOD BLEND

You and baby will both be better off, and so will your budget when you prepare baby's food in a blender.

Many young mothers think they must purchase baby food in jars and boxes. It's convenient, admittedly, but that's the only advantage I can see in using commercial baby food.

With your kitchen blender, or even one of those small inexpensive baby food grinders, you can prepare your own baby food, which will be less expensive. It will be fresh, more nutritious and tastier.

When your baby is old enough to eat baby food, blend up whatever you're having for your meal and feed it to your baby. There's nothing inconvenient about that. The quality of the food will be better and you won't have the added sugar or salt often found in commercially prepared baby food. (Many baby food companies are now cutting down on the salt and sugar and leaving their foods in a more natural state because of the national trend towards natural foods.)

For baby's cereal you need only to grind whole grain—rice, oats and wheat—into a fine consistency, add water, a little salt, and steam it. These grains can be ground in your blender. Baby will love it and it's oh-so-good for him, too.

From my own experience, I know that utilizing this one money saver has saved me hundreds of dollars. You will find it a great money saver too.

Money Saver Forty

DISPOSABLE DIAPERS—IS IT TIME FOR A CHANGE?

*At a minimum expense of over $700 to $1000
per baby each year, disposable diapers must be
purchased with disposable dollars.*

Figures from the U.S. Department of Agriculture show that the cost of rearing a child to the age of one in the United States is more than $10,000 a year. Part of this figure is based on child care, but a great amount of that money is spent on such things as formula, disposable diapers, baby wipes, cotton swabs, etc. A recent published study indicated some of the following statistics. Cloth diapers are $10 per dozen. Seven dozen will last through two babies for a one-time cost of $70.

The cheapest disposable diapers found were 30 cents apiece. At an average of 10 diapers a day (more for newborns, fewer for older babies), it comes to $3 a day, or $90 a month—a whopping $1,080 a year. Most children are in diapers until age 2 to 2½ or more. That figures out to be $2,160—$2,700, and twice as much for two children, as compared with $70 for cloth. You can save some money by buying disposables when they are on sale. If you do this you will pay about 22 cents apiece instead of the 30 cents.

Taking into consideration the cost of plastic pants, pins, electricity, detergent, bleach and softener, as well as time to wash, dry and fold cloth diapers, the difference between cloth and disposables is staggering. To match the price of cloth, disposables would have to cost less than a penny apiece. This says nothing of the environmental problems the disposables cause as they clog our landfills at an amazing rate.

The College of Family Life at a nearby university surveyed users of both cloth and disposable diapers to determine the actual costs of each. Expense, time, energy, baby comfort and personal preferences were considered. As you might expect, cloth users said cost was foremost in their decision, while users of disposables liked the convenience. Surprisingly, though, both groups ranked "less diaper rash" as the second reason for their choice, and "baby is more comfortable" as the third. Try wearing a disposable diaper for a day and see which you would prefer—cloth or paper. (Just a thought.)

Based on an average of seven changes each day, at 30 cents per diaper, the cost would be $14.70 per week, and $764.40 per year. Ten changes a day would cost $3 each day, $21 per week and $1,092 per year. Whether you conserve to seven changes each day or go for the ten, the cost still continues to take a big chunk out of the family budget.

Now the question is, where do most women buy their disposable diapers? Many will say that the supermarket is the place. While buying our groceries, we put a lot of the food dollar into disposable diapers. I would strongly suggest that those disposable diapers be taken from the food account and use our "food" money for food. Convenience is wonderful, but when one sees these figures $764.40 to $1,092, think of all the thousands of pounds of grains, legumes, nuts, dozens and dozens of cases of different canned goods, frozen fruits and vegetables, cases and cases of paper products that these dollars could be used for.

The decision is yours. If money is no factor then convenience is definitely worth it. For me, I used cloth diapers and kept the big savings. This money saver has been all but non-acceptable, but we leave it in for those in severe financial circumstance. We would have to say that disposables are more convenient and possibly more sanitary, but they are also more expensive and most Americans buy them with their food dollars. It is nearly unheard of to use cloth diapers, but we did it at considerable savings.

Money Saver Forty-One

SHOPPING STRATEGY IN THE BATTLE OF THE BUDGET

*Map out your plan of attack: The produce section first,
meat last—and skip some aisles altogether. Plan your
shopping—Shop your plan!*

Years ago, I discovered that the order in which I go through a grocery store makes a BIG difference in how much and what I buy. Therefore, I determined to have a method in the manner I shop.

To get the most for your food dollar, I suggest you follow a certain strategy. Head straight for the produce section and start there. You've gone through the newspaper and found leader produce buys (most grocery stores will feature some each week). You may now pick up many pounds of items at excellent prices.

For instance, if farmer-pack lettuce is selling for five heads for $1, I'll buy 10 to 15 heads. I figure I can pick the outer leaves off for the extra savings I get by purchasing farmer-pack vegetables. (Farmer pack means there has been no trimming.) The same lettuce will sell in another store trimmed, anywhere from 69 cents to 89 cents a pound. With the average head of lettuce weighing between one and one-and-a-half pounds, you can see that the savings are superb. One head of lettuce for $1 or five heads for $1. Which would you rather have? That's approximately an 80% savings.

Head next for the dairy section and load up on low-priced cottage cheese (I buy this on sale for 20% off), yogurt, milk and other desired dairy products. Since I used to purchase all our cheese through a co-op, I never had to buy cheese at the grocery store which gave me another savings of nearly $1.50 per pound.

If you buy breads, etc., go to the bread section next. If you make your own bread, however, a stop here is unnecessary.

Then it's on to the canned and frozen goods. If you've also canned and frozen your fruits and vegetables, you may not stop here either. If you use canned juices (natural and undiluted are best), pick these up now. If you use frozen juices and frozen products, stop by this section of the grocery store. (Hopefully, you read the ads and pick these up when they are on sale and stock your freezer.) Also, if there are leader items such as canned tuna or canned vegetables, buy the whole case instead of just a few cans.

Now, it's the meat counter. If you've been totaling your bill as you've gone along, you'll know about how you're doing—and you'll be much more conservative in your meat buying than if you'd come here first.

Notice, you have no soda pop, crackers, potato chips, convenience foods or other similar items. These are "money-eaters." If you've also taken boxed cereals off your list, you won't have to stop at that section. Look at all the money you are saving! Notice you have also passed by the cake mixes, jams and jellies because you've made your own, and the small packages—rice, beans, macaroni, etc.

Last, go for your paper products and cleaning supplies.

Don't panic! I'm not suggesting you abolish all those foods we've passed by, only that there are better ways to buy them as explained in other money-saver sections.

I also skip the spice section because I purchase spices by the pound and save 60-75%. I don't even go near the bakery department. I don't need to. You shouldn't have to either.

This gives you an idea of how YOU can enjoy greater savings by controlling your food dollars with a purposeful shopping strategy, thereby purchasing more "real" food with your money. Then, when you arrive home with your sacks full of groceries, you won't wonder, "What shall I fix for dinner?" or "What do I have to show for all that money?"

Remember...

- Devise a strategy that works for you, and then stick to it!
  My strategy is: "Plan my shopping and shop my plan!"
- Search the newspaper ads for leaders.
- Plan my menus.
- Make my shopping list based upon those menus and leaders.
- Take all these—ads, shopping list, calculator, and clip board—
  with you shopping.
- Shop in this order and total my bill as I shop.
    1. Produce
    2. Dairy products
    3. Breads and baked goods section (not the bakery!)
    4. Frozen and canned goods
    5. Meat counter
    6. Paper products and cleaning supplies

Money Saver Forty-Two

Clipping Clothes Costs

*Plan ahead, buy ahead. That's the key to buying highest
quality at the lowest price.*

You'll find it a good idea to make shopping for clothes a business.
The merchants make it their business. You too can learn some of the
tricks of the trade and avoid paying more than necessary for your family's clothing.

There are several ways to save you big money on your clothing
budget:

First, have a plan for buying your clothes just as you do for groceries. I make it a practice to keep a running inventory and record of
my family's clothing needs for the year—from underclothes to coats.
This way, it's easy for me to look ahead and take advantage of seasonal sales because I know our needs ahead of time.

For instance, when summer clothes go on sale mid-summer, I
already know my needs for the next summer, and purchase those summer items a year ahead. That saves big dollars. Obviously in the case
of children, you will need to buy in larger sizes, allowing for growth
during the winter.

Second, watch the paper for sales, particularly the seasonal sales,
and take advantage of them as they come along. One sale I always
watch for in July is the big annual family stocking sale at one of the
local department stores. At this sale they devote one large room to
nothing but socks—tables and tables of socks of every imaginable
kind. Some are seconds with a slight flaw, many times too minute to
detect. Some are surplus—too many of a kind—and need to be sold.
And some have nothing wrong with them at all. These stockings are
always marked down considerably; some as much as 60% or more.

At this sale I buy stockings for all ten members of my family for
one year. On one occasion I went to that sale and was able to get my

boys to-the-knee athletic socks for 99 cents a pair. They normally sell for $2.50 or more. That's $1.51 off—a savings of 60%.

For $1.19 I bought the girls beautiful argyle knee stockings ordinarily selling for $2.50 each—a savings of $1.31, nearly 50%. Little boys' athletic socks and dress socks were only 40¢ each. Men's stockings usually selling for $2.50 were three for $5—a 33 1/3% savings or one pair free.

When I approached the counter carrying three baskets full of stockings, I must admit it did look a bit strange. But I'm willing to endure some stares and chuckles for that kind of savings. For just over $50 our feet will be in excellent footwear for the entire year. If I bought these stockings on a need basis, paying the regular price, I would have spent as much as $150. Happy day! I only spent $50; saved $100—a 67% savings.

Third, don't wait until a special occasion comes along before you buy the clothes you want. It's all part of planning ahead. Let me explain. Stores advertise heavily for new Easter clothes; and of course, most little girls (and their mothers too) think they must have a new Easter dress. But the prices are at their highest on the new spring merchandise. Many parents will pay the high price because their daughter insists on an Easter dress.

Our daughters seldom get new Easter dresses (for several reasons), but they do get new dresses several times during the year. When a special occasion—Easter, birthday, graduation, etc.—is known to be coming up, I'll put it in the plan—my clothes-buying plan. When I see that special dress or suit on sale, I'll buy it several weeks or even months in advance. I must admit, however, the test is resisting the temptation of giving it to the person before the appropriate occasion.

Fourth, never buy anything on impulse. This goes for clothes as well as anything else. If there's something I'm thinking about purchasing that I haven't planned for, I give myself at least overnight to ponder and evaluate the purchase. Don't allow the emotion of the moment to dictate how much you'll pay. This is the time you need to be in charge of your clothing dollar just as you are your grocery dollar. It's wonderful how a good night's sleep and a new day will renew your resistance and wisdom.

For example, during one summer season I noticed a dress which appealed to me. The price was $54.95. It was exquisite and my impulse was to buy it immediately, even if the price was beyond my budget. I wanted it. I needed it. I deserved it. But, I decided to give myself time to think about it, which I did.

I still adored the dress after a week. So I started watching for the sales. It's after the Fourth of July when clothing stores bring in their fall merchandise and move their summer stock. Even so, the dress wasn't reduced. In fact, each time I passed through the store the next few days, the price held firm. Later, it dropped to $45. Still I waited. The middle of August, just before school, the price lowered to $39. A week later it was $34. I still didn't want to pay that much even though I was taking a chance someone else might snatch it up.

However, I was going on the principle that most people were buying fall and winter apparel. And there were two of the same dress, both in my size. I, however, was trying to buy ahead for next spring. It was not until after Labor Day that the store had its final summer sale. I walked in and there was the dress on the sale rack for $19.95! Of course, I purchased it—a charming dress for a charming savings—$36 off, a 64% savings. The style was new enough that it would not be out-of-date next season, and I had a new spring dress for $36 less than it normally costs.

Fifth, shop the factory outlets and bargain stores. In our area and in yours (check the yellow pages) there are factory outlets for women's sportswear, children's play clothes and girls' dresses. All items at these outlets are marked down from retail store prices. Sometimes the clothes are just an oversupply, or they may be irregulars and seconds. In any case, the markdown is always considerable. Seconds may be marked down for something as simple as an unsewn seam, or a flaw so small it's difficult to detect anything wrong at all.

There are also bargain shops that handle name-brand items with the label cut out. The savings on these perfectly good clothes can be as

much as one-third to one-half off the regular price. I've personally seen these sale pieces identical to retail pieces selling for half the price.

Periodically, these bargain shops will have special sales where they practically give their clothes away. For instance, one shop sent out a flyer advertising a New Year's Day sale where beautiful wool sweaters were offered at $5 to $8. My girls and I jumped into the car and went to the sale. We came away very satisfied having purchased six lovely sweaters at very little cost. I had two beautiful wool name-brand sweaters for a mere $8 each, an 80% savings over the $40 price I would normally have had to pay.

You can see that by following these easy suggestions, it's possible to make your clothing dollar s-t-r-e-t-c-h much further. Not only are you able to purchase quality clothing, but you are the one in charge of your clothing dollar and you're getting the most possible from it. For me that's important.

Remember...

• You be in charge.
• Plan ahead of your needs.
• Watch for sales (and buy only when on sale).
• Buy ahead of your needs.
• Never buy on impulse.
• Shop the factory outlets.

Let your motto be: "Never on Impulse and Always on Sale"

Money Saver Forty-Three

WHAT'S IN A SALE? DOLLARS FOR CENTS

By taking advantage of yard sales, garage sales, sidewalk sales, liquidation sales, and swap meets, you can make good use of the money you've already saved, and save again.

Because helping you save money in your shopping is the purpose of this book, we thought it appropriate to mention some sales other than food and clothing, which can save you even more of your hard-earned dollar. These are the yard, garage, sidewalk, liquidation sales and swap meets. Perhaps you've had experience with them, perhaps not. In any case, we think you'll learn ways in which these sales will save you more money than you thought possible.

Garage and Yard Sales. These sales are very popular in many parts of the country. Often you can find excellent items at very little cost. True, there is sometimes a lot of "junk" which you may have to sort through; but remember, "one man's junk may be another man's treasure." At garage and yard sales we've been able to acquire inexpensively some very usable furniture, toys, books, bikes and clothes (particularly children's clothing which is often like new).

If you've not been to a garage or yard sale, you might like to try it just to see what you can do in the way of picking up some usable items at a fraction of their value. At these sales, you're not shopping for "Sunday-best" quality, but quality nonetheless—items for camping, yard use, roughing it and playing. For example, in one such sale we watched a child's bicycle in excellent condition go for $5—a savings of $50 or $60.

Check the classified ads of the newspaper where these sales will be advertised daily. Or follow that sign you see posted on the street or stop when you see a sale as you're driving past. You never know what you might find.

Sidewalk Sales. Business neighborhoods, shopping malls, or businesses of an entire town often plan a certain day during the summer months when they will sponsor a sidewalk sale. The purpose is to clear out their unsold inventory such as summer clothing. The sale items are put out on the sidewalk on stands and racks for easy access to the passerby and shopper.

In our locale, sidewalk sales commonly occur following the 4th of July. Frequently the discount is significant and I've been able to find really good buys in clothing for my children and sometimes for myself.

As with all sales, you do need to exercise caution and wisdom. At times inferior merchandise will be included with quality items in the hopes of making it appear to be a good deal. Or, the substandard goods will be marked down drastically alongside quality goods that are discounted very little. Either way can amount to a lure to buy at not-so-low prices. The appropriate caution is, as always, "Let the buyer beware." But even with these pitfalls, I've been able to pick through the racks and find really good buys. With care, you can too.

Liquidation and "Going-out-of-Business" Sales. There are times,

especially in recent years when businesses, large and small, have had to call it "quits." In order to rid themselves of costly inventory and pay off their creditors, they will sell their merchandise significantly reduced. If you are alert to the sales in the newspaper and if you have money put aside, you can take advantage of them and can often purchase things you've always wanted but have never been able to afford. Or you may just want to buy ahead or replenish your storage.

Recently attending a furniture liquidation sale, we purchased a beautiful dining room table and six chairs for $900. This quality furniture would have cost considerably more had we purchased it under normal circumstances.

A word of caution. Beware abuse of the term "liquidation sale." Some merchants use "liquidation" to lure you into their store without any intention of closing shop. In such cases the sale discount may be insignificant and apply to inferior merchandise. "Let the buyer beware," is still good advice.

Swap Meets. Swap meets are becoming very popular. Here, a person is charged a fee or rent for space to "peddle" his wares, which consists of anything he wishes to trade or sell—used, made, bartered, purchased—anything and everything.

These swap meets are fun to attend and browse through and you may find some good buys on a limitless variety of things. Remember, you can buy outright or take something along to trade. The idea is a good deal for both parties.

Money Saver Forty-Four

Going, Gone, Gone! . . . To The Auction.

The auction can be an enjoyable,
exciting way to save big money.

Auctions are a great way to make some really good buys and have some fun in the doing.

The more experience you have with auctions, the better you'll be able to get the merchandise you want and with the big savings. Therefore, it is wise to take in an auction or two as a spectator to see how the auctioneer and his crew operate and observe the buyers. This will give you a valuable "feel" for auctions.

The first step, once you have searched your newspaper or become aware by other media of auction notices, is to prepare. If the ad lists the merchandise being offered, make a note of those items of interest to you. Then, and this is vital, jot down how much you are willing to pay for each item. This becomes your ceiling or limit for bidding.

Next, call the store and ask if it's possible to examine the merchandise before the auction. If so, make a pre-auction visit. While there, look around and take notes. If possible, have a friendly talk with the management or preferably the owner.

The owner is anxious to make as much money as possible above what it costs him to have a piece auctioned. He knows any auction offer will be at cost or below and that an additional 10-15% commission goes to the auctioneer, leaving his rock-bottom price. With that information, he may very well come down in price for you because it is a "win-win" situation. You win, he wins. Excellent savings for you and less of a loss for him.

At your first auction make a contract with yourself or spouse that you'll bid on something insignificant. This allows you a "rehearsal" that provides invaluable experience and gives you greater control of your impulses when you begin bidding on items of genuine interest.

Before the auction browse the entire store and take notes, listing the items of value to you in the order of desirability. This list may differ from the list made from the newspaper ad. Again, put a ceiling amount you are willing to pay alongside each item.

Before bidding, you will go to the main desk and obtain your bidding number and become familiar with the rules, policies, and purchase agreements. Some liquidators require a deposit which is refundable if no purchase is made. At this point, you are free to sit and review your information or mill around the store, until the action begins or until you are ready to participate.

Most auctioneers are very friendly and it's enjoyable to observe the whole scenario. Stories of auctioneers crediting you with a bid when you scratch your nose is simply not so. They have no desire nor ability to force a bid upon you.

However, the pace of an auction can be fast and rather hectic. The language is unique and may take some getting used to. Making the bid can be a source of anxiety for the beginner. Many bidders merely raise their number card (received at the main desk) to submit their bid, or raise their hand, point, or raise a finger. All you really need is to call your price aloud. That will avoid any question or doubt.

There is a tendency for buyers to keep bidding upward when the increments are small; that is, when the auctioneer raises the asking price by a mere $5 or $10 instead of $50 or so each time. So, know your limits and consult your notes and stick to your ceiling price.

Remember that regardless of the auctioneer's asking, you can respond with whatever bid you wish. If he jumps the asking to $100, you can offer $10. He may not like it and may not accept it, but if no better offer is given, he must honor your bid.

The auctioneer is there to make money and he does it by commission. The more he makes for the liquidator, the more for him. For that reason he uses every trick of the trade and will invariably start his asking price very high. After a brief sales pitch on the quality and worth of a piece and it's retail price, he will state an asking price of what may seem, on the surface, a good deal. Don't go for it. If you want to be the first bidder, start low, even ridiculously low. You have nothing to lose you can always bid more after you observe what the market action is. Or, let other bidders start off, and you will soon know the market and bid accordingly. Whatever, take your time and enjoy the experience.

Remember...

- Visit a couple of auctions just to watch.
- Prepare beforehand.
- Examine the merchandise before the auction.
- List your items in order of desirability.
- Write your top dollar next to each item listed.
- Bid only within the limit you have set.
- And, have fun!

PART TWO

BONUS TIPS FOR BETTER BARGAINS

Bonus Tip One

Are Coupons All They're Cut Out To Be?

Advertising would have you think you're missing a bonanza if you aren't busy clipping coupons, cataloging them, and adding up how much you've saved at the checkout stand. That might be the case, but I suspect the disadvantages may outweigh any advantages of dedicated "coupon-cutting."

First, it takes considerable time and consistent effort each day to go through papers, magazines, and mail, clipping, organizing and keeping track of expiration dates of coupons. Second, many other people, namely the grocer, the clearing house, and the manufacturer are making more money from these coupons than you can. Without profit motive, it is doubtful they would promote them. The price must be raised on couponed items in order to pay for the coupons that lure buyers into choosing that product.

Third, coupons may confine your choice to one brand and possibly a more expensive brand. That brand may not be to your liking. It may be a product you ordinarily wouldn't buy. Coupons sometimes require you spending so much on other items in order to save on one—which is not a savings at all. You are spending more money in the long run.

For instance, a store may run an ad giving you a free dozen eggs if

you purchase a certain kind of ham or bacon. You really didn't need or want the ham or bacon, which costs much more than the dozen eggs if you had purchased them at full price. Are you really coming out ahead in this game of coupons? That is the question. And a big question it is.

Yes, there may be people who make couponing pay (books have

been written about it), but they really have to work at it. I'd rather spend my time planning my shopping trips and menus than clipping coupons. However, I will clip if it's a coupon for an item I already use, and if the value is 50¢ or more.

What's more, it disturbs me when I see a good savings on an item, only to notice in the small print a limit of one or two per customer. It is not worth my time to go to a store for one can or package. If the coupon allows me to save significantly on a case or large quantities, I'll take advantage of it. Otherwise, I won't waste my time.

Refunds and rebates may also be worth the effort if the amount saved is more than a dollar or two. If to get one dollar refunded, I have to buy the product, save the receipt, send in the coupon (requiring a 32 cent stamp), wait for weeks to receive the check, then cash the check, it seems all that time and effort is more bother than the 68 cents ($1.00-.32 cent stamp) rebate is worth.

It comes down to time. You decide whether the savings in coupons and refunds are worth yours.

Bonus Tip Two

"MA'AM JUST HOW DO YOU PICK A GOOD MELON?"

Just how do you pick a good melon? For that matter, any fruit or vegetable? Let's take melons first. Most people have a hard time picking a good watermelon, cantaloupe or honeydew. Here are a few things to look for when buying these fruits, realizing that there is no 100% guarantee.

Watermelons. To pick a good watermelon is probably the most difficult of produce selection, unless the melon is cut. When buying a cut melon, however, be sure the flesh is firm and juicy and has a good red color. It should be free from white streaks and the seeds should be dark brown or black.

With uncut melons, look for the surface to be relatively smooth. The rind should have a slight dullness, not totally dull, but not shiny. The ends of the melon should be filled out and rounded and the underside should have a creamy color. Tapping your knuckle upon the melon should produce a full resonant sound; not hollow, but like a "full stomach."

The first indicator of sweet tastiness in watermelon is the "bee stings." It is said that when bees find a good watermelon they inject their stinger into the melon for its juices. After the stinger is removed, a little of the melon's juice seeps out and seals on the surface leaving a dark brown or black "scar."

I make it a point to look for these scars because I find that melons so inflicted turn out to be very flavorful, sweet, and juicy. To find the "bee stings" you sometimes have to almost climb into the bin and juggle the melons around. But it's worth it.

In performing this "watermelon search" I usually have a little audience of shoppers watching the fun and asking what I'm up to, and when I come out with my gorgeous melons, they ask me to pick one for each of them.

An alternative is to ask the produce manager to pick a good melon for you. Then, when you serve it and find that it isn't good, you can return it to him and request an exchange. A little "gutsy"? Yes, but why not? It's your money and hard-earned at that. Insist that it buys you quality merchandise.

Cantaloupe. There are three things I look for. First, the stem should be gone, leaving a smooth, symmetrical, shallow basin called a "full slip." If there is part of the stem remaining, the melon is not fully matured. Second, the skin between the netting should be a yellowish color. If that base is still quite green, the melon will probably not be ripe. Third, the netting or veining should be thin and coarse. It should stand out noticeably. Also, smell the cantaloupe. It should have the fragrance of cantaloupe.

If your selected cantaloupe is quite firm, it may not have reached its best eating stage. Put it on your kitchen counter for a couple of days at room temperature. This will allow it to complete its ripening. Refrigerate the melon a few hours before serving.

Honeydew. Look for a soft "velvety" feel. Ripe honeydew feels like velvet, green ones are smooth. There will also be a slight softening at the blossom end. If, however, it is too soft, it is likely mushy. There will be a faint aroma to the fruit and a yellowish white-to-creamy rind color. Signs of immaturity for honeydew are dead-white or greenish-white color and a smooth rind.

Other Fruits. The U.S. Department of Agriculture has established grade standards for most fresh fruits. Grade designations are often seen on citrus and apple packages and occasionally other fruits.

The grades are generally "U.S. Fancy," "U.S. No. 1," "U.S. No. 2," and "U.S. No. 3." The "fancy" grade means premium quality. A very small percentage of fruits are packed in this grade. "No. 1" means good quality and is the main grade for most fruits. "No. 2" is good. "No. 3" is the lowest grade packed commercially.

A shopper can usually make a good selection from the display counter without the help of grade labels simply by judging the external appearance of the fruit.

Here are a few tips I recommend. First, don't buy just because the price is low. Sometimes stores are trying to move out fruits which are old and will soon spoil. Check to see if there are breaks in the skin, or little starts of mold in hidden places such as the stem base.

Don't be fooled by the large nice appearing fruit. This may sound like a contradiction, but large sized fruits are not always the best quality or the best buy. What may appear to be a bargain may in fact be unsuited for your purposes; taste, for example. Appearance is very important in fruit selection, but it isn't everything.

Select fruit for the best taste possible. Occasionally fruit with an attractive appearance may have a poor eating quality because it is too ripe, picked too green, or has poor internal conditions like bruises. I find that when I ask the produce manager if he has tasted the fruit and if it is sweet, he will often cut a piece for me to taste.

I also carry a small paring knife with me when shopping. Especially if I am considering buying a whole case of fruit, I certainly want to know it is tasty and enjoyable. So I cut a piece and taste it. If it is good, I buy the case. If not, I buy only the one piece.

In this way I shop with certainty and remain in control. This taste test can be done in the store, or, if embarrassing for you, merely buy the single piece of fruit and taste-test it in your car. If you're happy with it, return and buy the case.

It is best to buy fruit in season. The quality is better. So is the price. Out-of-season produce is usually much more expensive except when used as a leader.

Another tip. I am not afraid to move boxes or cases in searching for best quality produce. I refuse to buy bruised or imperfect produce if I can avoid it. It is my money and I am paying for the produce. I therefore want the best the store has to offer. For example, if displayed bananas look too green or too ripe and bruised, I simply put that box aside and examine the next box. I continue the process until I find bananas that satisfy me. Do not be afraid to exert yourself even though the produce manager appears annoyed. Why should you buy unattractive or substandard fruit that he is trying to get rid of before he sells his best quality? Remember, it is your dollar. Be in control of it.

And what about vegetables? Vegetables add fiber, vitamins and minerals to the diet. They provide color and variety. I, therefore, want to say something about the importance of vegetables and offer a few tips in the purchase of these beautiful, luscious essentials of good eating and good health.

With vegetables freshness is important, first, last and always. Shopper, consider this. Does the vegetable look fresh? Is it bright and lively in its color and appearance? Is it firm and crisp? Beware of wilt, decay, mold, and breaks in the skin. Vegetables are really best in season.

Even though the federal law does not require the use of USDA standards for grades, there are some federal marketing programs which set minimum quality levels on some vegetables. Potatoes, onions and carrots are often graded. As in the case of fruits, grades for fresh vegetables are generally "U.S. Fancy," "U.S. No. 1," "U.S. No. 2," and "U.S. No. 3." "U.S. Fancy" means top quality and only a small percentage of vegetables are packed in this grade. Most are "U.S. No. 1" which is very good quality, "No. 2" is less and "No. 3" is the lowest grade.

In the National Academy of Sciences' anti-cancer diet, it is strongly suggested that we eat fresh fruits and vegetates abundantly. Also fiber. Vegetables most recommended are those rich in Vitamins A and C and particularly those in the cabbage family—cabbage, broccoli, Brussels sprouts, kale and cauliflower. These cabbage-family vegetables contain a cancer-inhibiting substance and their frequent consumption has been correlated with a diminished risk of some cancers, notably cancer of the colon.

Proper Storage And Care
For Fresh Fruits And Vegetables

For proper storage that shelf life may extend for fresh produce, the following are some ideas:
1. Pick fresh foods—not too ripe, nor wrinkled skin. Check for mold at place of the stem. Do not choose fruits and vegetables that were picked too green. Check to see if there are any breaks in the skin, and do not get produce that is bruised.

2. Choose produce that is "farmer pack" or that has not been watered all day to make it look fresh. You may have to ask the produce manager for unwatered produce.

3. When home, pack produce in clean "food storage" bags, and place a plain white paper towel in the bottom of the bag before placing the produce in. DO NOT WASH ANY PRODUCE before storing. Try to squeeze the air out of the bag and then tie with the bag tie. Store in a second refrigerator, if possible. (Pick up a used one at a yard sale.) If you do not have a second refrigerator, store in the back part of the refrigerator or in the vegetable drawers at the bottom of the refrigerator.

4. Do not store tomatoes in the refrigerator, nor pineapple. Find a cool place and store tomatoes upside down on a vegetable flat or tray so that their skins do not touch. Store pineapple upside down in a cool place in your garage or storage room. The same goes for bananas.

5. Do not store any produce on a cement floor. Put an old carpet down and store potatoes and onions in a box with an old blanket to cover them. They need air around, but they should not see the light or they will begin to sprout.

6. The thinner the skin or leaf of a food, the more important it is to use the paper towels when storing produce, as they will absorb the moisture which the fruit and vegetables produce. The harder the fruit or vegetable, the longer the shelf life in the refrigerator; however, you may need to change the bag and the paper towel if you are storing into the month, or even the second and third month.

7. Broccoli and cauliflower like to be stored in the coldest part of the refrigerator—almost frosty. Leave the wrapping on the cauliflower and do not put into storage bags, but place broccoli in bags.

8. All citrus—oranges, grapefruit, lemons, limes and tangerines can be stored in the garage in the boxes they come in for most of the year until the warm summer months. Then put them in the refrigerator. MAKE SURE THE LID OF THE BOX IS ON, or their peelings will dry out.

9. All squash except zucchini can be stored in the garage in a box on a carpet for the fall and winter months. The same for yams and sweet potatoes.
10. Store strawberries in the basket they come in and in a fairly cool place in a second refrigerator, if possible. Do not put in plastic bags, as they will mold.
11. Grapes should be stored in bags with the paper towel in a second refrigerator if possible. Watch them closely as they are thin skinned and touch each other.
12. Fruit such as kiwi, peaches, apricots, cherries, nectarines should be refrigerated and not washed. Bring peaches and nectarines from refrigerator a day or two before using so they can finish ripening.
13. Avocados can be stored in a cool place in the garage or storage room and they will ripen slowly.
14. Melons should be refrigerated, but not bagged.
15. Store apples in the box in the second refrigerator if possible.
16. All vegetables such as celery, lettuce, spinach, carrots, peppers, etc. should be stored in bags with paper towels.

Fruit and vegetables are much better for us and taste much better when used in season. They will always be more expensive when you buy out of season unless there is a special on them. Consider planting a garden and using the most fresh and delicious of all produce. Remember planting and using the produce from your own garden will actually free up $600 to $800 in a growing season.

And why are we doing all of this? For health's sake—to build the immune system—to avoid cancer and circulatory diseases. The National Academy of Sciences' Anti-Cancer Diet suggests that we eat 5-8 servings of fruits and vegetables daily. They are high in fiber, Vitamins A and C, and are good antioxidents. Once you begin implementing abundant produce into your daily diet,

you will probably see a big difference in your family's health. In addition to the health benefits, buying bigger, storing properly, and shopping less will free up "tons" of time as you begin using your home as your store and free up a tremendous amount of money as well.

I make it a practice to include as many fresh vegetables and fruit as possible into my lunches and dinner menus, which is easily done with fresh salads and vegetable and fruit trays.

Bonus Tip Three

Nutritionally Speaking

Not many years ago the thinking of most Americans was that food was food whether canned, frozen, dried, uncooked, baked or broiled. We weren't concerned whether it contained preservatives, was natural or processed, or even if it was "good" for us.

Times have changed. People are now taking notice of what goes into the food and what goes into their body. Many recent studies confirm that what we eat does affect our health, energy, vitality, and susceptibility to disease. In other words, "we are what we eat."

Food companies now stress the importance of their products being "natural," "whole grain," "having no preservatives," "no additives," and containing more vitamins and minerals, all seemingly for the public good.

This trend toward more healthful eating is a positive one. For over 35 years, I've based my family's eating program on the theory that what we eat does make a difference in our health and how we feel. So, of course, it's gratifying for me to see these studies confirm my practice. Following basic rules of good nutrition has given my family better health, less illness, fewer doctor bills, more energy, and a feeling of well-being. Obviously it hasn't happened overnight. The important thing is that it has happened. It is a daily, constant process.

Eating is more than merely filling stomachs. Maintaining health or regaining health should be the primary reason for eating. Who needs illness? We can accomplish so much more and enjoy life when we are free of disease with its pains and medications. That always-tired feeling might have something to do with diet, and so might the fact that some families seem to catch every "bug" that's going around.

Two broken arms, a broken finger, a hernia, eight deliveries, school physicals, and dental care—that's the medical history for over 35 years of our family of ten. Even colds and flu are minimal and pass quickly. It's my belief we must be doing something right. I'm convinced it's what and how we eat.

A recent study by the National Academy of Sciences produces eight do's and don'ts for an "anti-cancer diet."

1. Eat more fruits and vegetables, especially those rich in vitamins A and C.
2. Eat more whole grains.
3. Eat little or no salt-cured, salt-pickled or smoked foods.
4. Eat less fat and fewer fatty meats and dairy products.
5. Drink alcohol in moderation or not at all.
6. Keep calorie intake low.
7. Eat less protein, especially animal protein.
8. Eat more fiber-rich foods.

The diet is based on animal and laboratory experiments and on comparisons of eating habits of healthy people and cancer patients. To me, it is exciting that the ideas of the National Academy of Sciences support what I've been saying in this book about saving money while at the same time improving nutrition. Now doctors and dietitians widely publicize high fiber diets recommending we eat more fiber for better health and weight control.

A nutritionist in New York reports that fiber is the most natural way you can give your system a built-in form of immunity against most cancers. He tells his patients to have a bowl of whole-grain cereal—without salt or sugar—if they want to avoid colon problems, prostate gland trouble, and even the risk of systemic cancer. Fiber in whole grains increases bulk and reduces the concentration of cancer-causing substances in the intestine.

A New York university professor of nutrition endorses the whole-grain cereal breakfast, saying it protects against cardiovascular diseases. The extra water, bile acids, salts and fat bound by the cereal fiber act as solvents and remove possible cancer-causing elements from the blood.

People who eat whole grains also feel "full," so they are able to eat less and thereby lose weight. Experts agree that daily whole-grain cereals, plus an ounce of bran and an increased consumption of vegetables, legumes, fruits and nuts will provide more than enough fiber. The message is that we'll live healthier, happier and longer by having whole-grain breakfasts each day.

Recently, a team of doctors from the University of Naples was searching for a dietary treatment for victims having dangerously high blood cholesterol and triglyceride levels, which contribute to coronary heart disease. They found that people in southern Italy had less heart disease than either Americans or northern Europeans. Diet was found to be a major factor.

Southern Italians eat little or no meat or butter, but do eat large amounts of green vegetables, fresh fruit, pasta, bread and olive oil.

The doctors experimented with the diet of their high risk patients. They gave them diets rich in dried beans, vegetables, fresh fish, fresh fruit, vegetable soups, bread and very light in meat. The results were better than expected. Within two months, 40% of the patients had normalized blood lipid (fat) concentrations.

These studies and diets affirm what I believe and have attempted to say in this book. These money savers not only save you money, but are health-saving as well.

We try to use foods as much in their natural state as possible because it is nigh impossible to outdo "Mother Nature." The following chart and information gives an idea of what is contained in a kernel of wheat in its natural state.

The Wheat Kernel

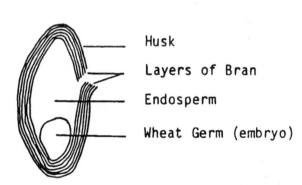

The wheat kernel is made up of three main parts important as foods, and the husk which is an outer straw-like covering also called chaff.

The bran layers contain large quantities of vitamins and minerals and a high quality protein. Among the vitamins known to exist in wheat bran are A, B1, B2, B6, Biotin, Calcium, Folic Acid, Inositol, Niacin, Chlorine, Vitamins C, E and G. among others.

Minerals include Calcium, Chlorine, Cobalt, Cholin, Copper, Iron, Fluorine, Iodine, Magnesium, Manganese, Phosphorous, Potassium, Silicon, Sodium, Sulfur, Zinc and other trace minerals.

The endosperm is a starchy substance containing protein, but very minute amounts of vitamins or minerals. The most common use for this part of the kernel is flour for making white bread.

Wheat germ is the life-generating part of the kernel and is reported to be one of the most abundant sources of Vitamins B and E in addition to quality proteins and fat.

When the grain is processed or milled much of the nutrition is destroyed or removed. Even though white flour products are "enriched" with some vitamins and minerals, many of the removed nutrients of the whole wheat are not replaced. Consequently "enriched" sounds good, but it is not what it used to be, naturally. A little research of whole grains will show what you may be missing if you are not eating them in their natural state. For the sake of good nutrition alone, you may wish to consider a change in your diet. Whole grains are truly "rich" in vitamins and minerals and they provide much of the bulk and fiber necessary in a proper diet.

You too can gradually change your family's eating habits, almost without them being aware of what's happening. You'll see gratifying results in your budget, in your health, and in peace of mind and freedom from stress as your family becomes more alert and energetic. You may also find yourself losing a few pounds as you gain better health through good nutrition.

Graduated Steps To Health And Vitality

1. Avoid alcoholic beverages, tobacco and drugs.
2. Avoid junk foods—soft drinks, pastries, candy and gum.
3. Avoid harmful condiments—table salt, refined sugar, salad dressings with unsaturated fats, and others.
4. Avoid, as much as possible, refined and processed foods and those containing fats and chemical additives.
5. Stay as close to nature as possible. Much of our diet should be raw fruits, vegetables, nuts and seeds.
6. Avoid overeating, even of good foods.
7. Become your own nutrition expert through study and observation.

8. Develop an appropriate exercise routine.
9. Search out further health practices until you have the maximum health and vitality you desire.

A Nutrition Philosophy

1. Start slow. Don't expect change overnight. Be consistent and develop a wise nutritional life style.
2. Read nutrition literature regularly to maintain interest and motivation.
3. Nutritionists sometimes disagree and contradict one another, as do proponents of other disciplines. To avoid discouragement from such controversies, identify the main ideas that remain constant with the majority of experts. Customize your nutrition approach to your own abilities and inclinations—something you can live with.
4. Avoid extremes, especially at first.
5. Read labels. Know the contents of what you consume.
6. Be discriminating in what you eat and drink. Never feel embarrassed or apologetic for refusing anything less than beneficial to your health. Your body is a miraculous mechanism. Care for it accordingly.
7. Do something nutritionally good for yourself and your family at least weekly. Daily would be ideal.

Think it over. The life you save may be your own.

"The doctor of the future with give no medicine, but will interest his patient in the care of the human frame, in diet and in the cause and prevention of disease."

— *Thomas A. Edison*

Some More About Nutrition

If you are buying and preparing the foods your family consumes, you are your "family's nutritionist" whether you have been trained in that area or not. As your family's nutritionist, you must address the question, "Am I feeding my family into *wellness* or *illness* by the things I buy in the grocery store and prepare in the kitchen?" As your family retires each evening, ask yourself the question— "Have I filled my family's stomachs or have I built and nourished their bodies and immune systems?" Even though you may not have been trained in food science and nutrition, there is much you can learn about the human body, the immune system, the vitamin and mineral content of good foods, and how they all relate in keeping the body from falling prey to the many viruses and unfriendly bacteria which seem to plague us today.

By accepting the challenge to read and study at least 30 minutes in the nutritional area once a week, the door will be opened, taking you in a direction where you will begin to understand the human machine and the care it needs to keep it in optimum health. You will then begin to apply your knowledge by way of implementing good health practices in your food buying and your meal preparation. You will want to have the philosophy stated by Thomas Edison years ago that "The doctor of the future will give no medicine, but will interest his patient in the care of the human frame, in diet and in the cause and prevention of disease."

You will buy and prepare your foods, always keeping in mind the National Academy of Sciences Anti-Cancer Diet, mentioned earlier in this book, especially emphasizing the eating of more fresh fruits and vegetables, and whole grains, which would greatly enhanced the fiber intake. Experts are now telling us that we should have a 40 gram fiber intake each day. The average American is lucky to consume 15 grams. I've found that I have to work at getting high fiber into our family's diet, but the rewards in better health are worth it.

Experts are also advising us to cut down our intake in the meats and dairy products so that we can keep our cholesterol low and avoid heart disease. We are also hearing that too much milk and dairy product consumption is being linked with several of our health problems. These are areas in which possibly a homemaker would wish to study more about and possibly make some changes in the types of foods her family consumes.

One of the major health concerns for Americans is the breakdown of the immune system. Many are finding themselves or family members diagnosed with such problems as EBV, Yuppie Flu, lupus, mono, yeast infections, etc., the ultimate being AIDS. Many mothers complain of their children's continual runny noses, colds, flus, earaches, coughs, etc. Why are we producing a generation of children whose immune systems are down and cannot seem to fight these illnesses which attack their bodies. For that matter, what has happened to our own immune systems and why are we finding so many young adults and middle-aged women and men who have deficient immune systems?

Eating three balanced meals a day may not be enough to counter the attack being made on our immune systems. It does matter if we eat white bread or whole wheat, hot dogs or skinless chicken breast, whole grain cereals or cold cereals. To help fuel our body for maximum immunity there are certain nutrients, vitamins and minerals which are a must in assisting the immune system with its work to keep us well. The important vitamins and minerals are A or Beta Carotene, C, E, and the B-Complex, potassium, zinc, iron, iodine, copper, sodium chloride, as well as the complete proteins and complex carbohydrates which keep our immune systems operating at optimum level. Water is also crucial for a good immune system, as well as a certain amount of good fats. When we deprive our bodies of any of these essential nutrients, the result is often illness.

We should know that the biggest cause of the breakdown of the immune system is stress. Too often, we cannot rid ourselves of our stress makers and thus we need to increase the quality of our food and supplement intake in the above mentioned nutrients, so that we can handle the stress we take in our lives.

Let's go over a brief explanation of the above-mentioned essential nutrients, how they work on the immune system and the good sources of foods where they can be found. Complete proteins are essential for the immune system to work properly. Proteins are complex molecules that are found in every living cell. In the immune system they form the antibodies and help structure the vital T-Cells and B-Cells. The absence of proteins in the diet reduces the ability of the immune system to function which thus allows the invasion of infectious viruses, bacteria, and parasites in the body. Proteins are found in many of our vegetables, nuts, beans, grains, seeds, meats, dairy products, and fish.

Complex carbohydrates are a must because they give us sustained energy as well as cellulose which passes through the system as dietary fiber and removes undigested and unused foods thus preventing bacterial back-up in the intestines. Good sources of complex carbohydrates are whole grains, breads, cereals and legumes.

We need a certain amount of fats, because they convert with the carbohydrates to provide an important source of energy. Our body fat also stores energy to meet emergency needs. If we have no fats, there is no energy reserve and the body draws from the protein supply which weakens the immune system. Fats are also required for the absorption of vitamins A, D, E, and K. Good sources of fats are the vegetable oils, such as canola, safflower, corn, soy, and olive oil.

The necessary vitamins are first Vitamin A or Beta-Carotene which keeps the skin healthy. The skin is a big line of defense against unfriendly invaders making vitamin A a must. Vitamin A also keeps mucus membrane surfaces moist. Vitamin A aids in efficient production of T-cells and aids the kidney filtration system in removing immunological debris from blood. Food high in Vitamin A are eggs, cantaloupe, apricots, yellow orange and dark green vegetables, dairy products and liver.

Vitamin C is essential because it affects the thymus and lymph nodes, and lowers histamine release, thus reducing allergic reactions.

Vitamin C stimulates the macrophages in the immune system to kill bacteria. Good foods high in C would be the citrus fruits, tomatoes, cabbage, strawberries, dark green vegetables, cantaloupe, potatoes, and papaya.

Vitamin E helps the body to remove harmful free radicals which injure the immune system, aids in the production of red blood cells, and speeds up T-cell reactions. Vitamin E also helps Vitamins A and

C to work better in the body. Foods found with Vitamin E are wheat germ, vegetable oils, whole grains, nuts, sea foods and sunflower seeds.

The total B-Complex Vitamin is essential, as it affects all the aspects of the immune system. B-Complex increases antibody responses, aids in energy release from carbohydrates, and helps in the production of hormones and steroids, as well as many other body activities. B-Complex also helps the body maintain bacterial-killing ability. Foods high in the B series are brewer's yeast, meats, whole grains, milk, eggs, legumes, nuts, brown rice.

All minerals are important—but high on the list of those needed for immune system enhancement are potassium, sodium, chloride, copper, iodine, iron and zinc. Potassium, sodium and chloride keep the body system in electrolyte balance. Potassium is essential to the proper function of the immune system. Good food sources of potassium are oranges, potatoes, bananas, avocados, raisins, meat, beans, milk, nuts, tomatoes, apricots, seafood and the winter squash.

Copper, found in cereals, nuts, legumes, meats, grapes and fish aids in energy-drive reactions in lymphoid cells. Iodine, found in seafood and kelp, is necessary for the manufacture of antibodies and aids the thyroid in the secretion of the immune control hormone.

Iron permits oxygen and carbon-dioxide exchange in body cells. It also affects the lymph nodes and energizes T cells and lymphocytes, all necessary for proper immune function. Foods containing iron are meat, blackstrap molasses, beans, nuts, whole gains, dried fruits, brewers yeast, spinach and potatoes.

A very important mineral, Zinc, which is found in whole grains, meat, eggs, legumes, nuts, keeps the skin healthy. It is a healer. A component of 100 enzymes, zinc affects the helper and suppresser T-cell regulation which is necessary for proper immune function. Zinc may be the immune system's most important mineral because it appears to be the most important for maintaining immune integrity. A shortage of zinc causes the thymus gland to shrink quicker than the natural aging process.

The body is like an electrically operated machine of which the immune system is an integrated part, depending upon electrical charges for its performance. Salt and water are two components that make it all work. If you eat a good diet, your salt and water balance will take care of itself. When you exercise vigorously, you must drink more water to compensate for that lost. When you find your muscles twinging and cramping this is an early warning that your body is out of proper salt-to-water balance resulting in a reduction of immune function. Sufficient water is essential. The body can survive for long periods of time without food, but only a few days without water. With prolonged dehydration the body is severely affected, the blood vessels begin to slow down, lymph fluid thickens and the immune system loses its main rivers for lymphocyte and antibody transportation. The body becomes more susceptible to bacteria invasion, viruses and parasites. Water also serves to regulate body temperature and lubricates the digestive process and cushions joint movement.

We can see that without these proper nutrients—proteins, carbohydrates, vitamins, minerals, fats, and water every single day, it is easy for our body's immune system to let its guard down, and become invaded with the unfriendly bacteria and virus. As we improve our nutrition, we also need to work through our stresses and problems, always trying to keep our mind and attitude positive. Adding proper exercise, we will be able to handle our daily challenges.

Another good health practice is to keep the fat intake low using only good fats so that our cholesterol count will be low. We should minimize the animal fats and use the good oils—canola, safflower, sunflower, corn, soybean, and olive. Avoid anything made with palm kernel or coconut oil. These two villains are 80-87% saturated fats. The good oils are high in polyunsaturated fats which help lower our blood cholesterol levels and thus reduce the risk of heart disease. Experts tell us that monounsaturated fats which are abundant in canola oil and olive oil are very effective in lowering cholesterol. A good rule to follow is to consume no more than 30% of our daily calories from fat and no more than 10% of our daily calories from saturated fats. The remaining 20% should be polyunsaturated and monounsaturated fats. Right now the average American diet contains close to 40% fat—which is way too high.

We should become oil and fat smart. Read all labels of processed foods—crackers, cakes, frozen dinners, snack foods and non-dairy creamers, as too often these foods contain the highly-saturated coconut and palm kernel oils, the worst of all oils.

Public-health officials tell of the dangers of eating high-fat, high-calorie foods and say that diet is implicated in 1/3 of cancer deaths and a great number of heart attacks. Individuals have different susceptibility to disease, and everyone may be more vulnerable at one time than another, but by changing our diet to 40 grams of fiber a day, lowering our fat intake, getting plenty of the whole gains and fresh fruits and vegetables, and cutting back on the animal product intake, we cannot help feeling better and seeing improvement in our family's health. A more healthful diet doesn't have to leave us feeling hungry or deprived. Actually by upping the fiber intake, we feel satisfied and full, and we can actually eat more of the right kinds of food. When we get sufficient minerals, we seem not to crave the sugar and chocolate foods.

Experts now tell us to keep our caloric intake low. This can be done by eating generously of the high fiber foods, the whole grains, fruits, and vegetables. We are also told to increase our Vitamin A (Beta Carotene), C, and E in order to boost immune function and reduce the risk of cancer and heart disease. These vitamins are considered antioxidant vitamins because they combat free radicals, which are toxic forms of oxygen released during metabolism that damage cell membranes, proteins, and DNA. The free radicals are the cancer producing substances which are in our bodies. Our cells have natural enzymes to combat free radicals, but over a period of time these enzymes cannot keep up with the damage caused by the free radicals.

There are other nutrients, vitamins, and minerals being studied which are linked with warding off disease and aging. Among them are folic acid which prevents precancerous changes in cervical cells and broken chromosomes, calcium and vitamins D and K for bone density, and B6 and zinc for immune function. It has been found that both caloric restriction and protein restriction do reduce free radical damage to DNA. Researchers are also finding that if caloric restriction is started before puberty, puberty is postponed, and delayed puberty has long been linked with longer life span.

The Basic Four Food Groups, which we have used as the backbone of good nutrition since the 1950's is now past history. We now have from the USDA a new nutrition pyramid which divides foods into five groups—breads and grains, fruits, vegetables, dairy products, and meats. Fats, oils, and sweets, which are not among the basic five, are at the top of the pyramid indicating we are to eat less of them. (See illustration) The pyramid shows how each group fits into a daily balanced diet with the base of the pyramid showing a heavy emphasis on breads and grains, and the next being vegetables and fruits (this graph supports the Anti-Cancer Diet).

Looking at the Food Guide Pyramid we see that we should build our diet from a base of grain products. It is suggested we eat 6-11 servings daily from the bread, cereal, rice and pasta food group. The USDA tells us to eat 3-5 servings of vegetables and 2-4 servings of fruits a day, 2-3 servings from the milk and meat groups, and eat the oils, fats and sugars sparingly.

By planning our food preparation according to the Food Guide Pyramid, we restore the grain products to their traditional place as the "staff of life." A good way to achieve the six servings would be to eat two or more servings of grain products at every meal. The grains are an excellent source of the complex carbohydrates, which supply the body with time-released, long-term energy. Putting more of these high-fiber grains into our diet gives us a sense of fullness and satisfaction and we therefore have less of the craving for the fat and sugar calorie foods.

As far as getting more fruits and vegetables into the diet, if you would think of adding five to eight servings of fruits and vegetables with your regular diet, it may be easier to accomplish your goals. Instead of striving to not eat certain foods, simply include more healthy fruits and vegetables with your regular daily diet. This will automatically help you cut back on less healthy choices. Just grab a glass of real orange juice rather than a pop, bananas and apples rather than chips and cookies. The benefits include a greater variety of nutrients, lower fat, and higher fiber. We do know that fruits and vegetables are high in nutrients that may prevent certain cancers. I actually like to think of my family getting at least eight vegetables a day and two or three fruits. Try it—you and your family will like it.

As you begin to study in any of these areas (30 minutes a week is my challenge for you), you become your "family nutritionist" and will probably want to make some changes in your family eating habits. What have you to loose? You then become a nutritional buyer, rather than merely a shopper, getting more buying power into your food dollar, and making your home become your store. *Then you, as the buyer, go to the store because you want to, not because you have to. This makes all the difference in how and where you spend your monies and how much money you free up to buy the "real" food.* You will find that you do have a budget sufficient to bring the "good" foods into your kitchen and into your family's diet resulting in improved wellness.

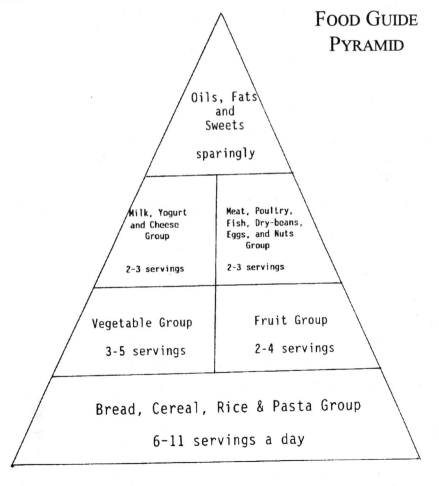

FOOD GUIDE PYRAMID

Oils, Fats and Sweets

sparingly

Milk, Yogurt and Cheese Group

2-3 servings

Meat, Poultry, Fish, Dry-beans, Eggs, and Nuts Group

2-3 servings

Vegetable Group

3-5 servings

Fruit Group

2-4 servings

Bread, Cereal, Rice & Pasta Group

6-11 servings a day

Bonus Tip Four

SPECIAL GIFTS FOR SPECIAL OCCASIONS: BE PREPARED!

Watch the sales and buy ahead for birthday parties and other gift-giving occasions.

Christmas is not the only holiday taking a big bite out of the budget. Valentine's Day, Easter, Thanksgiving and Halloween are also "budget busters." Mother's Day, Father's Day, birthdays and anniversaries are also expensive and need to be planned into the budget. Using the same money-saving ideas as we do for Christmas, we can save ourselves much money, time and frustration. The secret is to plan ahead and buy on sale before the happy day arrives.

With ten people in our immediate family, as well as sons-in-law and several grand children, birthdays alone burst our budget if I don't do some advance planning. When I plan my yearly budget, I include these occasions and sometimes I also note specific items I want to find on sale. It is not at all unreasonable to purchase an item on sale the week after Christmas to give for a future birthday or anniversary.

It's so convenient to have a supply of birthday party gifts on hand, items picked up at sales (only on sale, remember) where good products are offered at a fraction of the original price. It's easy to stock up on gifts for all these birthdays if you think ahead. Doing so saves the rush and last-minute shopping, saves in the cost of the gift, and in travel expenses, too.

In addition to the gift item itself, stores occasionally feature wrapping paper and ribbon on sale as well.

Use the same shopping principle with gifts as suggested for food—make your home your "store." It's amazing what you can have on hand when you plan in advance.

Bonus Tip Five

LEFTOVERS/BACK TO THE FUTURE

Whether preparing meals for one or two people or a group, it's hard to cook just enough for the meal and not have food left over. Not wanting to waste food, I've come up with a few ideas on using leftovers. However, one gets tired of having the exact same meal two or three days in a row—so "food coordination" (preparing new foods and adding leftovers) has helped me solve this problem.

We know that the more the food is reheated or recooked, the less nutrition there is; therefore we have to be careful not to overcook when using leftovers. I think all who manage a kitchen are guilty of putting leftovers in the refrigerator and having them get lost until the bad odor greets us as we open the door. The following are some of the ways we can eliminate wasting leftover foods.

First, in meal preparation, I'm always thinking of making today's preparations count for future use of other meals. It is time saving to prepare extra. For instance, if I'm preparing the bean dip, which is found in the recipe section, I prepare a large amount and use some for the current meal as well as make and freeze bean burritos. I freeze the remaining bean paste for future meals of tortillas, quesadillas, tostadas, etc. Also, when serving the Mexican casserole (in recipe section) a few days later, I will bring out the frozen bean paste and use along with the Mexican dish. This way one day of preparation extends into several meals.

When I have steamed, leftover vegetables such as carrots, peas, broccoli, squash, or corn, I put them into a little baggie and freeze the contents. Right before serving a homemade stew, I add the frozen veggies. Leftover, cut-up fresh fruit can be refrigerated or frozen for fruit smoothies and shakes.

Making extra soups or chili and freezing

the leftover for another meal on a busy day is a real time saver. If I do not wish to freeze the extra chili, I have a meal such as a potato bar and use the warmed chili with that meal. Extra spaghetti sauce, soups, or stews can be frozen for later use in other meals.

Leftover roast beef, turkey, and other meats can be used for future meals in stews, sandwiches, tacos, salads, casseroles, etc. A favorite and quick way to use leftover turkey and chicken is to layer gravy, turkey or chicken, and dressing in a casserole dish and bake for about 30 minutes. Right before serving place steamed broccoli on top. When we tire of turkey meals, I cube or cut the meat into strips and freeze in small baggies for future use in soups, tacos, salads, etc.

A favorite breakfast of ours is steamed, whole-grain, brown rice served with raisins, cinnamon and milk. If there is leftover rice, I will make a quick rice pudding for dinner. Leftover oatmeal cereal becomes a cake. My children have heard me say, "If you don't eat it for breakfast, you may be eating it for dinner."

The use of a freezer eliminates leftovers spoiling in the refrigerator. Using a little of the shelf space in the front part of the freezer allows me to see the frozen leftovers every time I open the freezer door. This reminder helps me to implement these foods into my daily meals. I also have a small shelf in my refrigerator for leftovers needing to be used up within a few days.

There are times when the vegetables and fruits in my refrigerator need to be used, and juicing is a great way to take care of this. If my family is not eating the vegetables and fruits, they are drinking them. Many times I make muffins or breads with leftover or extra fruits and vegetables.

Leftover brownies, cookies, or cake can be frozen and used when you don't have time to make desert for a particular meal. Leftover bread and crusts are good for making croutons, bread crumbs, or using in homemade dressing.

These are just a few ideas I have in using leftovers. Let your mind take off from here and create a few for yourself. One thing I do not do, and that is call them leftovers. Often families have an aversion when it comes to eating leftovers, so the trick is to add or incorporate them into other meals.

I have a rule of limiting meal preparation to 30 minutes or less except for a special occasion. "Food coordination" and cooking extra for future meals, helps me cut down the meal preparation time. As long as I'm making one casserole or one meatloaf, I might as well make two, one to use now and one to freeze and use later.

Solving the leftover problem with the use of "food coordination," saves me time, money and effort. Let's face it. Until you die, you will have to think of what to have for breakfast, lunch, and dinner. Ideas such as these help me with quick meal preparation, better usage of leftover foods, and less food waste.

Bonus Tip Six

THE CHEMICALS IN OUR DIET— DO WE NEED THEM?

Some of the latest statistics tell us that we the "average American" are putting about fifteen pounds of chemicals into our bodies through our foods each year. Just ten years ago that figure was five to seven pounds. Do we need these chemicals and for what purpose are they added to our foods. As we read food labels, we see words such as "additives" and "preservatives". What do these words mean to the American consumer? On my wall hangs a chart printed by the Center for Science in the Public Interest. It lists many of the chemicals the government allows in our foods. The chemicals are color coded—blue being unsafe, yellow meaning caution—still testing. The consumer will be informed five or ten years down the road if the chemical is harmful. The other color is green, meaning the chemical is safe for human consumption. My concern is that more than half of the chart has the color code of blue (unsafe) and yellow (may be unsafe).

Years ago when many of our foods came from farms, shopping was much easier; but food manufacturers have made chemical additives a significant part of the American diet. So many of our foods are manufactured and it seems that the manufacturers do not have our health as their all important goal. Their goal is to make a profit. Commercial food companies seem to have these questions before them when manufacturing a food.

- How can we sell a lot of this food and make a big profit?
- Can we put less in and still make it go further?
- How can we make the food taste good so that the consumer will eat a lot of it?
- How can we make it look better than it normally does?
- Can we extend the shelf life and have it not spoil before the consumer uses it, making it last for years without opening it?

- Can we pay a famous person a million dollars to endorse the product?

There are more than 8,000 chemicals being used in our foods. Are they safe? Some may be. Many are not. Many of the ingredients in our foods are "non foods." (Cream that is not cream, cheese that is not cheese, butter that is not butter, etc.) Sometimes it may seem as if food manufacturers are trying to make our foods better than Mother Nature. Our families are eating many of these "non foods" and I wonder what we are doing to our bodies.

What do some of these terms mean to you? "Anti-caking agents," "anti-foaming agents," "artificial sweetening," "azo dyes," "binders," "bleaching agents," "bulking agents," "coal tar dyes," "colorings," "dilatants," "emulsifiers," "flavor modifiers," "enhancers," "fillers," "jelling agents," "humectants," "hydrocarbons," "lubricants," "nitrates," "packaging gases," "preservatives," "release agents," "sequestrates," "solvents," "stabilizers," "starch," "tenderizers," "thickeners," It sounds like a chemistry lab.

Do you ever find yourself with the "I bet you can't eat just one" syndrome? Just as an example, the maker of a famous cookie spent millions of dollars developing a formula for that particular cookie so you can't eat just one. It contains 23 different appetite stimulants and 11 artificial colors. Putting fats into foods makes them weigh more. Many kinds of sugars, in one form or another, are put into foods purchased at the supermarket. If manufacturers were concerned about our health, they would not put the worst of all oils (palm kernel and coconut) into baby formulas. A famous baby-foods manufacturer was fined a great amount of money for putting colored sugar water into what they labeled "apple juice."

Some chemicals which are added to our foods and are not harmful would be "alginate," (seaweed or kelp) "alpha tocopherol," (Vitamin E) "ascorbic acid," (Vitamin C) "beta carotene," (Vitamin A) "calcium propionate," "casein," (milk protein) "citric acid," "EDTA," "ferrous gluconate," "gelatin," "glycerol," "gums," "HVP," "lactic acid," "lactose," "lecithin," and on the list goes. There are harmless additives that serve useful purposes. Be a good label reader and make the right choice.

Some of the things we should watch for and avoid are chemicals such as "sodium nitrite," "sodium nitrate," "saccharin," "artificial colorings," "BHA," "BHT," "sulfites," "MSG," "aspartame," "hydrogenated vegetable oil," (margarine) "caffeine," "BVO," "propyl gallate," "quinine," "sulfur dioxide," "sodium bisulfite," and others. Become a label reader and try to buy "real foods." Shop the perimeter of the grocery store. That is where you will find the "real foods" which have less chemicals added to them. The inner isles seem to have more foods displayed which I call money eaters, and wasters, and those foods usually have more chemicals added to them. One needs to become a "food detective" and look for the real food and buy less of the highly-chemicaled foods. Even the fresh produce has been sprayed, giving need for careful washing.

The goal for food preparation is to serve our family meals high in nutrition, which build the immune system. By loading the body with foods which have been highly processed and contain many food additives and chemicals, we defeat our nutritional goals. Our bodies were not made to take the abuse of a steady diet of chemicals. True, we may have strong constitutions, but sooner or later the chemical-cuisine diet may catch up with us in the way of serious health problems.

We Americans have demanded such foods because we are in a hurry and like the convenience. If we can pop the foods into the microwave and not dirty any dishes, we will buy them. Convenience foods are usually triple the cost but even more alarming is the fact they are highly-chemicaled and contain many non-foods.

Let's not be part-smart in buying foods which are stomach fillers.

Let's become label readers and buy foods which are high in nutrition, foods that will build the immune system, foods which have not been highly-chemically treated. My rule is: the less there has been done to a food, the better it will be for me and my family.

Bonus Tip Seven

MAKING MY HOME MY STORE

If you are the average American, four out of every five purchases you make at grocery stores or supermarkets are impulse buying. If you are the average American, you will spend about 35 minutes in the grocery store doing your shopping. For every minute you are in the store after that 35 minutes, you pay $1.89 more for your market basket. An extra eleven minutes more in the store can cost you an extra $20. Even though you and I shop with lists, we still are tempted to impulse buy. What is the problem? From the minute we place our hands on the shopping cart until our groceries are in our cars, the store has been massaging, cajoling, jolting and bombarding us with subtle and not-so-subtle messages designed to get us to buy what the grocer wants us to buy. Once we enter the store, the grocer's job is to try to control our every movement and shopping decision. Nothing sinister; they are just trying to sell us as much as possible—but usually, we the customer do not know or understand what is happening to us.

Don't feel bad, most of us are willing and easy targets for new marketing strategies. We love the one-stop shop (buy groceries, develop film, cash paychecks, make bank deposits, fill prescriptions, etc.).

I've found that if I become the buyer—not "Mrs. Shopper," and buy items I use when they are on sale, buying into the future and making the shelf life extend, then the trip has been well worth my time and I've made my money work for me. *Therefore, I go to the store because I want to and not because I have to and that makes all the difference in allowing me to get more buying power into my food dollar.* As I continue to do this type of buying, my home becomes stocked with foods and supplies I've purchased at a sale price.

Thus, when I prepare meals, I shop from my shelf and am always paying the lower price. I'm not running to the store in order to buy an ingredient or two to prepare the meal. For instance, if I wanted to serve orange juice, I go to my freezer and get a couple of cans, which

I have purchased by the case, paying $.50 cents a can. I'm not paying the price which the grocer would be dictating that I pay that day of $1.09 a can. My home freezer is storing the case for me and I pay the lower price. I also make it a practice of buying at least one case extra for my home store when I'm going to the market place, making the shopping trip worth my while.

In my home, I have a frozen food section (the freezer) a cold storage section (extra refrigerator), the canned, dried foods section, the dry goods section, (my storage room), etc. This frees me from going to the grocery store for every little thing—because I have every little thing in my home store. By making the shelf life extend for larger purchases of fresh produce, this alleviates me from continually running to the grocery store for bananas, milk, a head of lettuce, etc. I find the things that force me into the grocery store are milk, bananas, and sometimes fresh produce. When company comes, I visit my freezer, my refrigerators and my storage room and prepare the meal without running to the store.

This idea not only saves "tons" of money, but saves me a tremendous amount of time. Shopping weekly because there is nothing in the refrigerator makes me have to do everything over and over every trip. Why would I want to shop 52 times a year, when I could cut down the trips to 15 or 20 times?

To begin with, just think in terms of buying for two weeks, then the month, then for three months, six months, and for the entire year. By using my rule of always buying something for my home store, which extends into the future when going to the market place, it does not take long to have my home store stocked up.

Of course we are always using from the home store, but we are also replacing or restocking. A very important part of this idea is proper storage whether it be a head of lettuce or 50 pounds of oats.

Going to the supermarket when you want to (because there is a good buy) not because you have to, makes all the difference. You will find that you will soon have a lot more food on hand, as well as save more of your time, money, and energy.

Bonus Tip Eight

SOME "FOOD FOR THOUGHT"

Never at the expense of good nutrition do we want to save money, because we will either pay the grocer or the doctor. But just how much are we willing to pay for a pound of bananas? In the market place we could pay anywhere from $.29 a pound to $.59 a pound. Buying ten pounds of bananas can cost us $2.90 or $5.90 if we aren't "street smart" in using the supermarkets as they serve us and not letting the merchants dictate the price we are going to pay for our bananas or anything else we wish to purchase.

As a buyer, there are some things we should know about supermarkets. First the design of the store is not haphazard—it is on purpose. It is laid out so that we will spend as much as possible on what the store wishes us to buy—which is often more than we came for. Could it be why those "quick" trips to the market for a "gallon" of milk could cost us about $25. With four of those trips a month, we can easily blow over $100 of our food budget and have very little to show for the money we have spent.

Some foods are so profitable that they command their own aisles—such as, you guessed it—breakfast cereals, soft drinks, etc. It is not coincidence that we almost always have to walk through the produce department when we enter a supermarket. Produce is the second most profitable section in the store, the first being meat. The fact that milk is often at one end of the dairy case and butter at the other is no coincidence. Stores like to "anchor" a display by putting popular items at each end.

The meat, poultry and seafood displays are at the back of the store so that we'll see them every time we emerge from an aisle. Could that be why the most profitable section of the store is the meat counter?

And what do we know about the "prison" aisles, about traffic flow, turbulence shopping and the boutiques? Then there is the scan scam. Recently researchers in southern California found that close to one out of every ten scans was wrong. Three out of four mistakes favored the supermarkets. Studies show that scanning errors may be costing shoppers more than one billion dollars a year. Would it be good for us to know our prices, watch the scanner display, and pay particular attention to "sale" items.

Now don't get me wrong. I love every merchant that will offer me a good buy and he will find me in his store when that is the case. But in order to be more than "part-smart," I do need to know what I'm dealing with when I walk into a supermarket. I need to be skilled and determined so that I get the best buy and the highest quality at the lowest price. I want to use the stores as they serve me, and not let them dictate the prices I will pay for my grocery items. When I leave the supermarket, I need to know that I did get my money's worth and that I do have a lot of merchandise to show for the amount of money I've spent.

Bonus Tip Nine

ALTERNATIVE GROCERY STORE SHOPPING

As a buyer, I want high quality at low prices. The question I ask myself when I need to purchase an item is, "Where is the best place to buy the item for the least amount of money, always getting the highest quality merchandise?"

If I wish to purchase 50 pounds of oats, there may be six or seven places that sell oats by the 50 pounds, and there will be six or seven different prices. I never buy oats in the small packages, because we use a lot of oats and I save a major amount of money by purchasing them in the larger package.

Another example would be spices. Buying spices in small containers at a grocery store becomes too costly and they are not as fresh as I like them. Containers of spices have sometimes been stored in a warehouse for several months and then been on the shelves of the grocery store for more months. By the time I would buy them, they would not be very fresh or potent. But, I have another plan and that is that I use small group buying. Some friends and I or my daughters and I will order them from a spice and herb company. By buying by the pound, it is much cheaper. By calling in a combined group order, I will get a price break for the merchandise. The company will UPS the order right to my door. The advantage is that I have a superior product, buying spices and herbs once a year, and have spent far less money (and no out-of-state tax).

This is my thinking by purchasing my items this way—if I can buy something once a year and be done with purchasing that item, why would I want to buy the item 12 times a year or 52 times? Whether I've had four or ten mouths to feed, the benefits are the same.

When buying apples, I can go to the nearest grocery store or I know of a place about a half hour's drive from here that I can buy any kind of apple for $10 a case. If I were to buy the same apples in the grocery store, they would cost $25 to $37 for the case. My apples have been stored in controlled atmosphere storage and are very crisp and tasty. Recently I bought three cases which lasted for three months. When I put apples in lunches, I just go to my second refrigerator and not the grocery store.

If I wish to buy pinto beans, I usually take a short drive and make the trip worthwhile by buying the beans as well as other beans and grains by the 25 or 50 pounds. I buy enough of these items to last for a year. If I use an item, buying it once a year at the best price and getting high quality saves my time, money and effort.

PART THREE

HELPFUL EQUIPMENT
AND APPLIANCES

HELPFUL EQUIPMENT AND APPLIANCES

There are some marvelous kitchen appliances which will be useful to you in making the most of these money-saving ideas.

Throughout the book I've made mention of several pieces of kitchen equipment which I consider musts in helping me save time and money. In fact, many of these small appliances have now been combined into one machine with attachments which will do the work of several small machines. Whether you have several small appliances or one large one with attachments or whether you are just beginning and have only one or two, those you don't own needn't cause you to think you must go out and buy them all immediately. Put them on your list of things you need. Keep an eye on the newspaper ads for a good buy. As your savings increase and the right opportunity comes along for that appliance, buy it and use it as presented in the money-saving section. It has taken me several years to acquire some of my appliances, but I assure you they are worth the planning and waiting.

Blender.

I use this kitchen aid for so many things that truly I'd be lost without it. I was able to pick up an excellent blender on sale recently at half price (50% savings). I use it in making cracked wheat, rice, and other grain cereals for breakfast. It is invaluable in food canning and preserving. It's handy for preparing dried fruit delectables such as fruit leather. You with babies can make your own baby food by simply blending fresh fruits and vegetables and other foods direct from the table. A blender makes it all possible with ease. I have a friend who uses her blender to mix powdered milk. Non-instant powdered milk mixes well in the blender and tastes better than instant powders. Uses for a blender are endless.

Wheat Grinder.

This is another indispensable appliance. If buying wheat in bulk and making your own bread appeals to you, a grinder is a must. Whole wheat flour can be purchased, of course, but it is so satisfying to grind your own, adding it fresh to the bread mix, and thus enjoying a much-improved nutrition in your baking.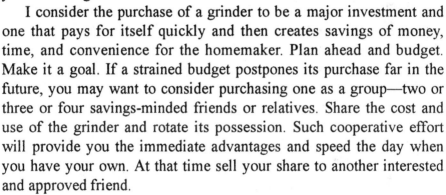

A wheat grinder, or grain mill, is excellent for grinding any grain. Corn for cornmeal. Rye for rye bread. It may also be used for cereals —rice, wheat, oats and others of your choosing.

I consider the purchase of a grinder to be a major investment and one that pays for itself quickly and then creates savings of money, time, and convenience for the homemaker. Plan ahead and budget. Make it a goal. If a strained budget postpones its purchase far in the future, you may want to consider purchasing one as a group—two or three or four savings-minded friends or relatives. Share the cost and use of the grinder and rotate its possession. Such cooperative effort will provide you the immediate advantages and speed the day when you have your own. At that time sell your share to another interested and approved friend.

Bread Mixer.

When making your own bread, you can knead it by hand (as I did for many years) or you can use a bread mixer. A mixer certainly takes a lot of time and effort out of bread making. It's so handy to just add the ingredients and turn on the switch. In 10 or 15 minutes the dough is ready to put into pans. The attachments on my mixer also allow me to make cake and cookie dough, taking the tiring muscle work out of all my baking.

Hand Mixer or Counter Mixer.

If you do your own baking, it is essential to have either a hand mixer or a larger counter mixer. The small hand mixer can be purchased at a minimal cost and you may find it sufficient for your needs. If, however, you wish to invest in the larger counter mixer, you can use the hand mixer until such time as budget and opportunity (sale) allow.

Electric Slice-grater.

My slicer is not very fancy, but it slices, grates and cuts into all sizes and shapes. I find it so handy in the preparation of fresh vegetables, saving much of the time required by hand slicing or grating. I've not found it necessary to have a more diversified processor with its many additional uses. If you do a lot of cooking from scratch, it may be you will want a more versatile machine. There are those that grind and mix as well as grate and slice. You'll need to decide what is best for you and your needs.

Food Dehydrator.

Essential if you do much drying of fruits and vegetables. There are several types of dehydrators. An air dryer is good, but its use is subject to the weather—rain, wind, dust, and pollutants. Your oven makes a good dehydrator, although a bit cumbersome and costly. It also adds heat to an already summer-hot kitchen. I've even dried fruit out on our roof, but with too many limitations and inconveniences to like the method or recommend it. I find the commercial food dehydrator to be the most useful, quick, and convenient.

Juicer.

I've used a juicer for years. I don't consider it an absolute necessity, but it's so nice to drink the fresh juices it makes possible. Our favorite fruit juice is apple; our favorite vegetable juice is carrot. A splash of celery juice enhances both—delicious, refreshing, and nutritious.

Personally, I wouldn't be without a juicer because of all the canning and freezing I do. Additional attachments make it possible to enjoy an interesting variety of things like making peanut butter and especially ice cream, also family favorites.

Food Processor.

Lately the food processor has become a popular tool which actually takes the place of several small kitchen devices. The food processor will shred, chop, slice, blend, knead bread, crush ice, etc. With a wide range of speeds, it helps make cooking pleasant and enjoyable by accomplishing those tedious time-consuming tasks quickly and easily.

Its use depends upon your needs, however. Even though my processor will mix bread, its capacity is only one quart, so I prefer using my bread mixer which mixes enough dough for four loaves. Notwithstanding its limitations, the food processor is becoming commonplace because of its versatility and efficiency, which allows the homemaker to do a lot of from-scratch cooking without a long time in the doing.

Yogurt Maker.

With yogurt the favorite it is, a yogurt maker is a good appliance to have. It is inexpensive, easy to use and with a little experimenting your family can enjoy an abundance of tasty and nutritious yogurt treats.

Other helpful kitchen devices include...

- electric fry pan,
- wok,
- electric knife,
- Crock-pot,
- cherry pitter,
- apple peeler,
- steam juicer and
- ice cream maker.

The pitter and peeler come in handy with canning or dehydrating fruit and the steam juicer for canning fruit juices. We seldom buy ice cream, preferring to make it at home with our choice of favorite ingredients and flavors, natural and nutritious.

In short, if a piece of equipment will help me perform my kitchen labors quicker and easier, I need it. Savings in time, as well as money, is vital.

There may be other useful kitchen appliances which you have or feel you need that I haven't discussed. I've listed those which have proven valuable to me and make my work in the kitchen easier and more productive, which is the idea behind any kitchen appliance. I suggest you acquire, by careful planning and budgeting, those appliances you consider to be most helpful.

Appliances are the tools of your trade. Remember, your home is your business. Acquire tools to help you gain greater control in the successful management of your home—greater savings of money and time, with convenience and ease.

Nothing complicated about Big Savings when you know how! ...and the how of it is now in your hands.

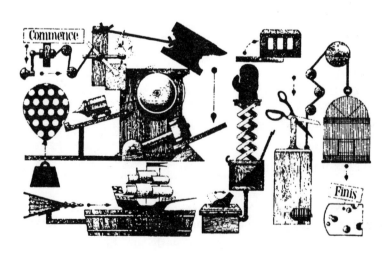

PART FOUR

LET'S TALK IT OVER

From the testimonials of our readers and seminar participants, we know first hand the help these money-saving ideas give many, many people. Lives are literally turned around, improved financially, improved in the management of homes, and improved in health and vitality.

To assist you in getting started with the development of your own savings philosophy and in putting the money savers to work, we have included this section.

We also recommend "Jil's Savers' Seminar," an invaluable tool for keeping up to date on the latest information and techniques and maintaining motivation and efficiency in your money-saving adventure.

Peace of mind, tranquillity and financial security are what this book is all about.

DO THE MONEY SAVERS REALLY WORK? YOU BET YOUR BUDGET!

When all ten of our family were home, a national study indicated the average family of four in the $20,000-$25,000 income bracket spent $300 each month for food, an average of $75 per person. At that time we were not the average family of four but we fit in that statistical profile in income only.

With our eight children at home (six teens), we allowed ourselves $45 a month per person for food and housekeeping incidentals—soaps, cleaners, paper products, etc. This was a savings of at least $30 per person below the average family of four.

Some wondered how we were able to do this and still not skimp on good nutrition. It is a fact that feeding more does decrease the percentages a small amount if you become a buyer and not the shopper. After having read about our Money Savers and Bonus Tips, you know our "secrets." These Money Savers as well as other ideas are a way of life with us, and yes, they really do work. Because of these Money Savers, we were able to live and eat very well. Indeed, we believe we have eaten much better than the average family.

Figures may drastically change with inflation, but the principles are the same. We have seldom done without or scrimped. We've enjoyed an abundant and rich variety of foods—fresh fruits and vegetables year-round (foods many families skimp on because they can be so expensive), plenty of fresh fruit snacks, plenty of meat, fowl and fish, nutritious whole grains, and quality dairy products. We have never sacrificed quality for economy in our foods.

How did we do it? It's all in the use of the Money Savers and Bonus Tips as explained in this book. They are our success, tried and true, for over thirty-five years. And they will work for you. We guarantee it! Applying these Money Savers, as described in this book, you will save big money.

Why, when you apply even one Money Saver or Bonus Tip, you will see the benefits immediately. Imagine then what will happen as you apply all the ideas! The savings over a week, a month, a year will astound you. So, give them a try, you've nothing to lose and everything to gain.

DEVELOPING A SHOPPING PHILOSOPHY

Have you noticed the intensity with which businesses advertise, as if their lives depended upon the success of that ad to bring in hordes of customers. As a matter of fact, the businessman's life does depend on advertisement. It is his means of getting you into his store where his service can make you comfortable while buying his product, the quality and price of which will keep you happy enough to return again and again.

The ads are the lure. They must get your attention first and then make you feel you can't pass up their bargain and product benefits. That's why advertising seems to be promising you the world—best prices, best service, best product, best everything.

Sounds good, doesn't it? Well, they can't all be the best in all aspects of their business in their particular line of product or service. And they aren't. Some are better than others in one or more aspects—service, product or price.

Most businesses, grocery included, are competitive if not equal, in some or most of those basics. Quality and cost are critical variables and you, the customer, will never know how they vary without some effort on your part.

You notice how advertisements are structured to make you believe that the product is the cheapest and best quality of all its competition. It could be true. If that ad convinces you it is true, that the sponsor has the best product at the best prices with the best service to you, you will likely try it out. And if you are happy with the results of your purchase, you'll probably continue shopping that store.

But often we let service and quality obscure the cost variable.

It may well be that you can receive equal service and quality for less. No one is going to tell you. You have to dig out the facts yourself. Remember the football game analogy—and the battle of the budget. It's real. He, your friendly businessman—opponent, wants to win and win big. He must win to survive. And we want him to win, but not so big that it is at our unaffordable loss. The idea is for both to win; he enough to prosper and you enough to prosper. You aren't able to know his financial situation, but you do know yours and its your purse that lets you know how you are doing in the battle of the budget—winning or losing.

To win, to do comfortably well in the game, you must become as intent on getting the most for your money as the grocer is intent on getting and keeping your business. This intensity on your part is what we call your shopping philosophy—whether the shopping be for food, clothes, properties or luxuries, it is the same—you must be a smart shopper.

The bottom line is, now and always—you pay the difference, the difference caused by your carelessness, your mistakes, your apathy, and yes, your trusting nature.

All this business intensity doesn't mean you can't enjoy shopping, or be friends with your grocer. Just the contrary. A wise shopping philosophy puts you in control, and a person in control is confident, happy and friendly. The whole purpose of a shopping philosophy (and this book) is to help you save big money and enjoy doing it.

So how does one go about developing this all-important shopping philosophy? This book of Money Savers is, in and of itself, a shopping philosophy, but a proper attitude must compliment the Money Savers. Attitude is all important. Be success-minded; know these saver ideas can and will help you win financially. Be confident, happy.

Be in control, in control of what income you do have, be in control of managing your home, in control of shopping. The Money Savers will put you in control especially if you prepare and plan. Set goals. Prepare for your shopping trips. Plan a budget. Know your abilities, needs, costs and priorities. Get excited about what you are going to do, the improvements you are going to make. Read the newspapers, mailers, etc. Come to understand what the advertiser is trying to cause you to think and do. Analyze him, his ads, methods, store layout. Become an expert.

Keeping records is an important part of your philosophy. They are the score keeper and tell you how well you are doing. Make your home your business and be the best home-manager possible. Take pride in yourself and your work—your home business.

Be alert to changes and trends. Glean money saving ideas where, when and from whom you can. Share your ideas. Join with others. Make saving money a way of life, an automatic reflex. We know that adherence to the suggestions in this book will make a big, happy difference for you. We know you can do it. Our best to you. Success in savings!

How Much Have You Saved?
Only Your Record Really Knows!

Many people dislike record keeping and refuse to do it, especially household-management record-keeping chores like developing and maintaining a budget, recording expenditures, and computing and comparing. Admittedly it is not the most exciting of activities, but it is one of the most important in saving you money.

Remember, your home is your business. To be successful in business, you must keep records. It is the only way of knowing exactly and quickly how the business is succeeding, where the money is going, how much you have saved. It's risky business trying to keep it all in your head. Only your record really knows. Without records, you are flying blind.

Proper and thorough records keep you in control and eliminate confusion and doubt. Records allow you to know if you are winning the battle of the budget and by how much; what your gains and losses are, your needs and surpluses. You will be amazed at the difference in your attitude as a result of the control that comes from keeping adequate records.

As with the Money Savers and Bonus Tips, so it is with records; start small and expand gradually. A sudden burst out of your comfort zone could cause you frustration and discouragement.

Some keys for successful record keeping are consistency, accuracy, neatness and simplicity. Ideally you will set some time aside each week to plan and record. Consistently record the expenses of each shopping trip. Shop with a clip board in your hand and make notations as you go. You will also have your guidelines, budget and ads attached to that board.

One of the best assurances of accuracy is to consistently record pertinent information in its proper place and as it happens. When shopping, for example, record your expenditures as soon as possible after leaving the store. Tally the expenditures of all stores you've shopped upon returning home. If family demands won't allow it, take

five minutes before the day is over
to put all figures onto your records.
This will do wonders for your success.

Neatness of handwriting is
essential, as is neatness of keeping
records. Take a few minutes and get
organized. Know where things
belong. Have a set place for your
records. Honor your organization by
replacing records to their designated
location immediately after use.
Frustration is alleviated and hours of
time saved.

Keep your system and your records simple. Customize them to
your own needs and liking. Don't worry about how someone else does
it or about what things you are not doing. Just do well and enjoy what
records you are processing. With time you'll improve and expand your
skills. Computerizing your records is great if you can, but not necessary.

Try keeping records for one month. As you begin to actually see,
on paper, the savings you're making, you'll never stop. Seeing is
believing. And saving money is really believing! How much have you
saved? Only your record really knows!

A Dollar Saved Is More Than A Dollar Earned

It is often difficult to realize how true and how important this maxim is. It has also been said that if we don't develop a habit of saving money on a regular basis, success is not possible for us. We believe there is truth in these words.

There are two basic ways to save money. One is to put money aside in a "nest egg" or savings account. The advantages of this method are the interest it earns you (if in an account) and its availability—it's there when you need it. A vital warning! Never touch your savings for other than their intended purposes.

We suggest a separate account for each savings objective or goal, three being essential: an emergency account, an "items on sale" account, and an investment account. Use the emergency account for emergencies only—unemployment, hospitalization, etc. Use the "on sale" account for those things you have been planning for—furniture, appliances, etc. And use the investment account only for your investments—real estate, stocks, bonds, etc. The advantages of these savings accounts are many and obvious.

Paying less than the current asking price is the other way of saving; the method we devote this book to.

In your search for savings, consider these facts:

Earned money requires...
• Effort, hard work, fatigue
• time, inconvenience, demanding schedules
• taxation and other deductions commonly eroding up to 50% of take-home pay.

Money saved requires . . .
- no effort
- none of your time
- no taxation or other consuming deductibles

Money saved is all yours, free and clear. You can use it to earn additional monies through savings accounts and investments, increase life's goods, or to indulge yourself with pleasures and luxuries. But it's yours, free from demands and obligations.

Think it over. Think what you could do with the extra "income" of savings. That's what this book is all about—saving you big money. Yes, A DOLLAR SAVED IS MORE THEN A DOLLAR EARNED.

A Dollar Saved is more than a Dollar Earned!

Tax Free. . . no tax!

Labor Free. . . no labor!

HOW TO PUT THESE MONEY-SAVING IDEAS TO WORK

Now, after reading the book and becoming excited with all the possibilities the money-saving ideas have for saving you money, you may feel a little bewildered wondering how to start and where. The whole idea, of course, is to begin saving money now—immediately.

The money saving sections of the book are methodically presented under the general headings of "Get Ready...Get Set...And Go!", the idea being that preparation precedes action. You may want to begin your money-saving, chapter by chapter, in that logical sequence.

Or you may prefer to jump in now and be on with it. If that is the case, do it. You have nothing to lose. But start small and proceed slowly. Select a money saver that appeals to you. Reread that section. Outline the essential steps. Adjust those steps to fit your own style and personality. Chart your course. Then go for it.

Having enjoyed the success of one money saver, select another, and yet another until you are familiar and effective with all of them. In the doing, you will discover and develop money-saving ideas of your own. Capitalize upon those ideas. Refine and improve them. Include them in your own shopping philosophy and money-saving methods.

"Jil's Savers' Seminar" is a great way to yet started. In it you'll receive the latest in trends, economic conditions, ideas, suggestions and an enjoyable friendship.

May success and good fortune smile generously upon you. I know they will.

WITH A LITTLE HELP FROM FRIENDS

Share your money-saving efforts with a friend or two. Any self improvement project, regardless of how desirable and worthwhile, can be difficult and discouraging when attempted alone. With pleasant company the effort succeeds and is fun. We all need support and encouragement from someone who believes in us and will help us progress, someone who sees our potential in spite of our weaknesses and mistakes. That support and encouragement is more effective coming from an active participant who's in the "game" with you.

The effect is exhilarating when friends are right alongside you, comparing notes, planning together, brainstorming new ideas and ways to implement them. You'll find yourself laughing over silly mistakes and sharing the elation of success. Momentum increases, as do enthusiasm and opportunities to save and share.

The old adage is true: "Two heads are better than one." We think you'll discover you're having such great fun and success together, you'll want to invite more friends to join in. Our response to that is, "Great! The more the merrier!"

Your financial worries...
Can now be over!

DEBT: MONSTER OR SERVANT?

You got a monster eating up your income?

It seems appropriate in a book on saving money and home management to say something about debt. Debt may be likened to a surgeon's scalpel, a life saver when used with skill and discipline, but lethal in the hands of the untrained.

The warning to avoid debt as a plague is appropriate for most of us most of the time. Using debt to solve financial entanglements is often economic suicide and contrary to what is presented in this book.

The reasons are simple and subtle. Many use credit cards or other easy credit plans to obtain something they want for pleasure or to take advantage of substantial savings. The use of credit becomes easy and convenient. Before they realize what's happening the credit habit is established and a lifestyle has developed. Many, if not all, purchases are soon being made with the card and buyers are caught in the "buy now, pay later" cycle which becomes, for many, a pit of quicksand.

When buying on credit becomes a habit, more is likely being spent than is earned. The debt balance steadily increases with outrageous interest rates of 18-21% (plus an annual privilege fee of $20 for some cards) ticking away with unrelenting regularity as dangerous as a time bomb.

A very wise person once said: "Interest never sleeps nor sickens nor dies...once in debt, interest is your companion every minute of the day and night; you cannot shun it or slip away from it; you cannot dismiss it; it yields neither to entreaties, demands, or order; and whenever you get in its way or cross its course or fail to meet its demands, it crushes you." (J. Reuben Clark) Another quote reminds us that "Thems that understands interest receives it; thems that don't pays it." (L. Tom Parry)

Day and night, unnoticed, it continues its demands, eating into future earnings and ability to repay, ever threatening you with loss by default, loss of your security—home, business and property. And loss of contentment, peace of mind. Loss of ability to catch up, to save, to live within means. Loss of ability to make the "good life" for yourself and family. For these reasons we would advise caution whenever considering borrowing whatever the purpose. Beware the debt monster!

A local state extension service has given the following good advice regarding credit:

1. Don't use more than 20 percent of your take-home pay for debt payment, other than your home mortgage.
2. Your total outstanding debt (other than your home mortgage and auto loan) should not exceed one month's take-home pay.
3. Don't use more than one-third of your yearly discretionary income for credit. (what you have left after paying all your necessary costs, such as food, housing, clothing, transportation, and medical.)

The following are some questions to ask yourself if you suspect you are in credit card danger:

1. Are your expenses growing faster than your income?
2. Do you post-date checks or send checks to creditors without signing them to gain extra time?
3. Do you have less than three months' take-home pay put away for an emergency?
4. Are you taking money from savings to pay for credit charges?
5. Are you taking out new installment loans before the old ones are paid off?
6. Are you paying bills in 45 or 60 days rather than on time?
7. Are you taking cash advances on your credit card to cover regular living expenses?
8. Are you working overtime to cover credit charges?
9. Do your installment loan payments equal more than 20 percent of your monthly take-home pay?

10. Are you making only minimum payments on your installment charges and continuing to charge new items?
11. Are you perilously close to the debt limit on all your charge cards?
12. Do you overdraft your checking account?

On the other hand debt can be a wonderful servant if used judiciously and sparingly. Many excellent investments are possible because of it. For most, home ownership is impossible without borrowing. Debt can earn you money, provide needs and wants and luxuries. It can accomplish its services almost as quickly as the legendary genie.

Again caution. The secret of proper use of indebtedness is good judgment in determining your needs, limits and abilities. Apply wise guidelines. Use debt sparingly. Don't borrow against something you haven't got. Don't borrow at the risk of losing money or possessions you can't afford to lose. Don't borrow against anticipated increases in income. Such increases have a way of disappearing. In some cases job loss or relocation have cruelly replaced such illusionary hopes.

A safer servant is savings. Our continuing advice is to follow the Money-Saving methods presented in this book. Start with what you have rather than with what you have not. Your chances for success will be much greater and the journey more comfortable.

Trapped in a financial maze? Here is your way out!

PART V

RECIPES AND MENUS

Part V offers a sampling of over 100 of our favorite recipes; recipes which are tailored to our money-saving philosophy. Nutritious and delicious! Included in the recipe section are a few of my children's favorites which they use in their meal preparation. We think you will find them as enjoyable as we have.

Also included is a sample two-week menu planner to help you get started planning your meals. Meal planning will save you time and frustration while providing your family the best in quality, nutrition and a tasty variety.

Our five daughters are now married and running households of their own. It is my joy to see them incorporate into their lives things they learned at our home. It's great to watch them work with their own children and I enjoy talking with them on an individual basis about meal preparation and the health of their little ones. We often use our own "good deal group" (implementing seasonal shopping) to purchase foods in small group buying. We order spices, pastas, grains, beans, nuts, dried fruits, honey, fresh produce, etc. together for big savings. This way we are able to afford to stock our "home stores." Small group buying allows us to make many once-a-year purchases, thus eliminating buying the same item over and over again in smaller quantites.

As you make menu plans, record them in the menu section of your kitchen business book. You will find it helpful to have these menu plans on hand. Rotate them about every six or eight weeks. Your family will not remember when you used them last, and rotating will save you time thinking up new menus each week. Using seasonal menu plans is another good idea. Menu rotation also provides a happy variety and prevents boredom on the part of the cook and diners.

MENUS
Two-week Menu Planner

RECIPES
Breads, Rolls, Muffins
Breakfast Ideas
Cakes, Cookies, Bars, Ice Cream, Yogurts and Desserts
Soups, Salads and Sandwiches
Main Dishes

Two Week Menu Planner

	Breakfast	Lunch	Dinner
Monday	Oatmeal; raisins & milk; whole grain toast; bananas & grapes; sunflower seeds & almonds	*Tuna Salad Sandwich with lettuce; carrot & celery sticks; apple; *Whole Grain Jam Squares	*Taco Salad; watermelon, cantaloupe, honeydew fruit plate; corn chips; grape-lemonade drink
Tuesday	*The Best of Granolas; milk bananas, strawberries & grapes; *Whole Wheat Muffins, honey butter	Tomato, lettuce & mayonnaise sandwich on toasted bun; carrot & celery sticks; sliced oranges	*Whole Wheat Crust Pizza; tossed salad with Italian dressing; garlic bread; grape juice; *Yogurt Sundaes
Wednesday	Whole grain brown rice cereal; honey, raisins, cinnamon, nutmeg, bananas; whole wheat toast	Tuna salad—lettuce, green onions, cucumbers, celery, radishes, tomatoes, with lemon & oil dressing; *Blueberry Whole Wheat Muffins; *Mrs. A's Fantastic Cookies	*Stir-Fry Chicken With Pea Pods & Rice; fruit cup (bananas, grapes, peaches, strawberries, pears, & coconut)
Thursday	Cracked wheat cereal; honey, raisins, milk; fresh sliced peaches; *Whole Wheat Buttermilk Muffins	Avocado, tomato, sprouts, lettuce sandwich on rye; cucumber slices, pepper slices, carrot sticks; *Zucchini Bread	Crock-pot roast beef with potatoes, carrots, celery, onions; tossed green salad; *Fresh Apple Cake with whipped cream
Friday	*Whole Wheat Waffles; jams and/or syrups; milk, fresh fruit cocktail	Toasted cheese sandwiches; dill pickle, carrot & celery sticks, sliced tomato; *No Bake Cookies	Baked chicken breasts; steamed broccoli, cauliflower, & carrots; cottage cheese-pineapple salad on lettuce leaf
Saturday	*Whole Wheat Pancakes; fresh strawberry jam, fresh peach jam; milk	Roast beef, tomato, lettuce & mayonnaise sandwiches; nectarines; vegetable sticks; *Lemon Bread	*Spanish Fiesta; tossed salad, Thousand Island Dressing; sliced melons; orange-pineapple lemon drink
Sunday	Scrambled eggs; Sizzlean, orange juice, *Whole Wheat Orange-Nut Rolls; milk	Baked halibut with lemon & tartar sauce; *Potato Casserole; cabbage salad; green peas; cherry cheesecake	Fruit supper: plate of several kinds of fruit (melons, peaches, strawberries, grapes, apples, oranges, etc.); yogurt; cottage cheese; whole-wheat crackers; almonds, sunflower seeds

*Recipes in Part Five: Recipe Section

TWO WEEK MENU PLANNER

	Breakfast	Lunch	Dinner
Monday	Germade; honey, raisins, milk, whole wheat toast; sliced oranges	*French Onion Soup; croutons, grated cheese; tossed salad, dressing; *No-Bake Cookies	*Enchilada Steak & Everything; vegetable tray with dip; fruit cocktail with sliced bananas
Tuesday	Six-grain cereal; raisins, honey, milk; *Whole Wheat Muffins; grapes	*Roast Beef Sandwich Spread on whole wheat toast with lettuce & sprouts; tomato, pickle; *Raw Apple Bread	*Turkey Salad Supreme; fruit plate; hot whole-wheat rolls; *Vanilla Yogurt with fruit sauce & nuts
Wednesday	Whole wheat French toast with frozen jams and/or syrups; milk; grapefruit	*Lentil Soup; *Whole Wheat Bread Sticks & butter; vegetable sticks; *Whole Wheat Macaroons	*Chicken Broccoli Casserole; orange Jell-O with shredded carrots; frozen corn; *Whole Wheat Carrot Cake
Thursday	*Granola; milk; bananas, grapes, strawberries; cinnamon toast	*Apple Sandwich; *Banana Bread; yogurt; milk	*The Greatest Beef Stew; French bread; apple-carrot celery Jell-O salad; fruit plate with lemon dip
Friday	Boiled eggs; whole wheat toast; orange juice	*Cream Cheese Sandwich Filling sandwiches; apple; carrot sticks; fruit yogurt	*Clam Chowder; tossed vegetable salad with *Yogurt Dressing; hot rolls; frozen fruit dish (peaches, strawberries, raspberries, grapes, & bananas)
Saturday	*Family-Favorite Breakfast (rice cereal); raisins, nuts, cinnamon, nutmeg; milk; bananas, strawberries	*Tuna Salad Sandwich; vegetable slices grapes, banana; *Pumpkin Bread	*Lemon Chicken; brown rice; chow mein noodles-fresh fruit plate; *Yogurt Ice Cream
Sunday	*Whole Wheat Waffles; frozen freezer jams, syrup, butter; fresh fruit bowl; milk	Texas cut roast beef; creamed peas & potatoes; tossed vegetable salad; corn-on-the-cob; bottled raspberries with whipped cream	*Crispy Chicken Salad; rice; fruit & cheese plate *Whole Wheat Caramel Brownies

*Recipes in Part Five: Recipe Section

BREADS, ROLLS, MUFFINS

Whole Wheat Bread

3½ c. milk	1 T. salt
2/3 c. vegetable oil	1 c. water
2/3 c. honey	4 eggs
4 T. dry yeast	12 c. whole wheat flour (+ or -)

Scald milk and cool slightly. In a small bowl dissolve yeast in 1 c. warm water. To the cool milk add salt, oil, honey, eggs, and yeast mixture and mix well. Sift flour and add just enough to make the dough the consistency of a cake. Let stand 15 minutes. Add more sifted flour until mixture is too thick to stir with a spoon. Work with hands and then turn out on floured pastry cloth. Knead for 10-20 minutes (by hand). Bread mixer can be used. Put back into bowl and let rise until double in size (about 45 minutes). Divide into four pieces and shape into loaves. Place in buttered loaf pans. Cover and let rise till double in size. Place in oven and set at 350°. For better rising, do not preheat oven. Bake for 45 minutes to 1 hour. (Powdered milk and hot water can be used in place of regular milk. Use 3½ c. hot water and 1 c. powdered milk.)

Variations...

• *Cinnamon rolls:* Use above recipe and if you wish add about 1/3 c. more honey for a sweeter dough. Roll out dough and spread 2/3 c. melted butter and 1 c. brown sugar, 1 T. cinnamon mixture. Sprinkle with 1 c. raisins and ½ c. chopped nuts. Roll and slice. Let rise and bake for 20 minutes in a 350° oven.

• *Orange-nut rolls:* Follow cinnamon roll directions. Instead of sugar and cinnamon mixture, mix grated peeling of 1 orange with 1 c. sugar. Add 1 c. chopped nuts. After cooled, frost with a powdered sugar frosting, substituting the juice of 1 orange for the milk.

• *Bread sticks:* Break off small pieces of dough (about golf-ball size) and roll into long ½ inch wide sticks. Roll in sesame seeds and bake for 20 minutes.

Whole Wheat Bread or Rolls

3 T. yeast in 1 c. warm water   1 T. salt
2/3 c. honey or 6 T. sugar   1 c. powdered milk
1 c. oil   4 c. warm water
8-10 c. whole wheat flour

Mix all the ingredients. Dough is proper consistency when it is slightly sticky. When mixed in bread mixer, dough should come off the side of the bowl, leaving it clean. Divide into four pieces and shape into loaves. Place in buttered loaf pans. Cover and let rise till double in size. Bake in 350° oven for about 40-50 minutes until golden brown.

Miriam's Oatmeal Bread

2 c. oatmeal   Pour water over oatmeal
4 c. boiling water   and let cool
1 1/3 c. brown sugar
6 T. vegetable oil
2-3 T. yeast disolved in 2/3 c. warm water

Add sugar, vegetable oil, and disolved yeast to oatmeal mixture.

Then add:
10 c. flour (white or whole wheat—less if whole wheat)
4 t. salt

Mix together and let rise for 1 hour. Form dough into loaves and put into oiled bread pans. Let dough rise another hour. Bake at 350° for 30-35 minutes. Makes 4 loaves

Mignonne's Bread or Cinnamon Rolls

½ c. warm water	2 t. salt
2 pkg yeast	2 eggs
1½ c. luke warm milk	½ c. soft shortening
½ c. sugar	7-7½ c. flour
	(white or whole wheat)

In a large mixing bowl put yeast in warm water. Add sugar, and let yeast disolve completely. Add each of the other ingredients one by one, with the flour last. Mix for 10 minutes in bread mixer. Let rise once in bowl. Punch down and shape into 2 loaves, place in bread pans, and let rise again. Bake at 350° for 25 minutes or until lightly brown. For cinnamon rolls, roll out the dough and apply soft butter and sprinkle with mixture of 1 t. cinnamon and 1½ c. sugar. Roll, shape, cut, and place on oiled cookie sheet and let rise again until double in size. Bake in 350° oven for 8–10 minutes. Frost with powdered sugar frosting. Cream cheese can be added to your frosting mix.

Honey-Nut Whole Wheat Orange Rolls

2 T. dry yeast	2 t. salt
½ c. warm water	4 eggs, well beaten
2 c. milk, scalded	9-10 c. whole wheat flour*
1 c. margarine	4 T. orange peel, grated
2/3 c. sugar	½ c. orange juice
½-¾ c. honey	1 c. crushed walnuts

Soften yeast in warm water. Scald milk and combine with margarine, sugar and salt in large mixing bowl. Cool to luke warm. Stir in 4 c. of flour and beat with electric beaters until very smooth. (If you have a bread mixer, use that to mix the dough.) Add beaten eggs, softened yeast, grated orange peel and the orange juice. Add remaining flour, a little at a time to make a soft dough. Cover and let rise until double in size (2 hours). Punch down, cover and let rest 10 minutes.

Roll dough in rectangle, ½ inch thick. Spread with 1 cube softened margarine and 1 c. sugar. Roll into a jelly-like roll, always rolling toward you. Seal edge and slice in 1" thick slices. Place the roll slices on a baking sheet, pressing the roll to form an oblong shape rather than round. Put 1 t. honey and a few crushed nuts on top. Cover and let rise about 45 minutes. Bake at 400° for 12–15 minutes. Frost with a margarine, orange juice and powder sugar frosting. For an alternative you can use sugar, cinnamon and raisins.

*Substitute ½ c. of whole wheat flour with ½ c. gluten flour for a nicer roll.

Lemon Bread

½ c. vegetable oil	1½–2 c. whole wheat flour
1 c. brown or white sugar	(or white)
2 eggs, slightly beaten	1 t. baking powder
½ c. milk	¼ t. salt
1 c. powdered sugar	½ c. finely chopped nuts
grated rind & juice from 2 lemons	

Cream oil and sugar together and add eggs. Sift together flour, baking powder, salt and grated lemon rind. Bake 50 minutes to 1 hour at 350° in oiled loaf pan. Remove from oven and top (while hot) with mixed lemon juice and powdered sugar. Cool and slice with electric knife.

Raw Apple Bread

1 c. brown sugar	1 t. nutmeg
1 c. whole wheat flour	1 egg
1 t. soda	¼ c. vegetable oil
½ t. salt	1 c. nuts (chopped)
1 t. cinnamon	2 c. grated raw apple, unpeeled

Sift dry ingredients together. In medium mixing bowl, combine egg and oil and beat together. Add apple and nuts, then gradually stir in dry ingredients. Spoon into 1 large loaf tin which has been greased and bake at 350° for 50 minutes. You can put into two small loaf tins and bake for 35–40 minutes. Do not peel the apples when grating.

Zucchini Bread

1 c. white sugar	1 t. salt
1 c. brown sugar	1 t. baking soda
3 eggs	1 t. baking powder
3 T. vanilla	3 T. cinnamon
1 c. oil	¾ t. cloves
3 c. whole wheat flour	1 t. nutmeg
3 c. raw grated zucchini squash	1 c. chopped nuts

Beat sugar, vanilla, oil and eggs together. Add flour, salt, soda, baking powder and spices. Stir in zucchini, nuts and pour mixture into two greased loaf pans. Bake in 325° oven 1 hour. Glaze with lemon and powdered sugar glaze or milk and powdered sugar glaze after removing from the oven.

Banana Bread

2 c. whole wheat flour	1 t. soda
1 c. brown sugar	¼ t. salt
½ c. vegetable oil	3 ripe mashed bananas
1 egg	¾ c. nuts

Cream butter and sugar; add beaten egg. Mash bananas with a fork and add to first mixture. Add flour, soda and salt. Add nuts. Pour into oiled loaf pan. Bake at 350° for 1 hour or until done.

Whole Wheat Pumpkin Bread

4 eggs, well beaten	1 t. baking powder
3 c. brown sugar	2 t. soda
2 c. canned pumpkin	1½ t. salt
1 c. salad oil	1 t. allspice
2/3 c. cold water	1 t. cinnamon
1 c. nuts, chopped	1 t. nutmeg
3½ c. whole wheat flour	1 t. cloves

Cream sugar and oil. Add beaten eggs and water. Sift all dry ingredients and add to first mixture. Continue to beat and add pumpkin and chopped nuts. Pour into 2 greased loaf pans and bake at 350° about 1 1/3 hours or until done. This may be served plain, frosted or with a glaze.

Whole Wheat Muffins

2 eggs	3 T. brown sugar
1 c. milk	3 t. baking powder
¼ c. vegetable oil	½ t. salt
2 c. whole wheat flour	

Heat oven to 400°. Grease muffin tins or put cup cake papers in muffin tins. Beat eggs and stir in milk and oil. Stir in the remaining ingredients until flour is barely moist. (There will be lumps.) Fill muffin cups about ¾ full and bake for 20 minutes or until golden brown. Remove from pan immediately and serve with honey-butter or homemade jams.

Variations...

- *Buttermilk muffins:* Decrease baking powder to 2 t. and stir in 1/3 t. baking soda with flour.
- *Blueberry muffins:* Stir in 1½ c. fresh or 1 c. frozen, thawed and well-drained blueberries with the milk. Before baking, sprinkle

with mixture of ½ c. brown sugar, ½ c. chopped nuts and
1 t. cinnamon.

- *Apple-nut muffins:* Stir in 1 medium grated apple with the milk and 1 t. cinnamon with the flour. Sprinkle tops with ½ c. brown sugar, ½ c. chopped nuts and 1 t. cinnamon mixture before baking.
- *Cheese muffins:* Stir into batter 1 c. grated cheddar cheese.
- *Date-nut muffins:* Stir in ½ c. pitted chopped dates and ½ c. chopped nuts with milk.
- *Granola muffins:* Decrease milk to ½ c.., flour to 1 c. and sugar to 1 T. Stir in 1-2 c. granola with flour.

Kristine's Pumpkin Muffins

1 c. honey	Mix first 4 ingredients
½ vegetable oil	in a bowl
4 eggs	
1½ c. cooked pumpkin	
2¾ c. whole wheat flour	Mix next 7 dry ingredients
¼ c. wheat germ	and add to the wet mixture
1½ t. baking powder	
1 t. soda	
½ t. cloves	
¾ t. cinnamon	
½ t. nutmeg	
1½ c. raisins	Stir in raisins and nuts
1 c. nuts	

Put batter into greased muffin tins, or cake papers and bake at 375° for 15 to 17 minutes. Cool and serve. Makes 2 dozen. (Vitamin E Rich.)

Miriam's Basic Muffin

1 egg	Mix first 4 ingredients
½ c. vegetable oil	
1/3 c. sugar or honey	
¾ c. milk	
2 c. flour (whole or white)	Add next 3 to wet ingredients
3 t. sugar or honey	
½ t. salt	

For variety, add 1-2 T. poppy seed, or drop 1 t. raspberry jam in middle of each unbaked muffin and top with a mixture of brown or white sugar, cinnamon, flour and butter. Shredded cheese stirred into the batter is also good. Be creative and try your own combinations. Drop the batter into cupcake papers in muffin tin and bake 20 minutes at 350°.

Miriam's Zucchini Coconut Pecan Muffins

1 scant c. vegetable oil	1 t. salt
2 c. sugar (I use fructose 1½ c.)	1 t. soda
3 beaten eggs	1 t. cinnamon
3 c. shredded zucchini	1 t. baking powder
2 t. vanilla	1 c. coconut (shredded)
3 c. flour (whole wheat or white)	1 c. chopped pecans

Mix the wet ingredients in large bowl and add all the dry ingredients, coconut and chopped pecans in that order. Bake in pre-heated 325° oven for 20–25 minutes or until lightly brown.

Whole Wheat Cheese Appetizers

1 c. shredded shrp chdr cheese	1/8 t. cayenne pepper
1/3 c. butter	¼ t. salt
1 c. whole wheat pastry flour	

Combine all ingredients in mixing bowl and gather together with hands in a ball. Shape in roll 1¼" wide; chill. With serrated knife, cut in 1/8" slices. Bake on ungreased baking sheets in preheated oven 8-10 minutes. Makes about 4 dozen.

Apple Oat Bran Muffins

1½ c. oat bran	½ c. skim milk
½ c. whole wheat flour	1 egg
3 T. brown sugar	2 T. sunflower or soy oil
3 T. honey	½ c. apple juice
2 t. baking powder	1 c. shredded apples (don't peel)
½ t. sea salt	2-3 T. raisins
1 t. cinnamon	¼ c. chopped nuts, almonds preferred

Preheat oven to 400° Blend egg, skim milk, oil, apple juice and raisins in blender and set aside. Mix oat bran, flour, brown sugar, baking powder, salt and cinnamon in separate bowl Combine both mixtures and add shredded apples, stirring until moist Bake in oiled 12-muffin tin pan for 20 minutes or until light brown.

Mashed bananas can be substituted for apples or use half apples and half bananas A mixture of flour, brown sugar, butter, cinnamon and chopped nuts can be sprinkled on the top of each muffin before baking.

Breakfast Ideas

Family-Favorite Breakfast

    1 c. whole grain brown rice   4 c. cold water
    ½ t. salt

    Served with:
    Raisins, cinnamon, nutmeg, honey, milk.

Place 1 c. of dry brown rice in blender and blend until fine. Put 4 c. cold water into the top of a double boiler and add ½ t. of salt and the ground brown rice. Place water into the bottom of the double boiler and bring the water to a boil after placing the rice mixture pan over the bottom part of the double boiler. When the bottom water is boiling, place a lid on the rice mixture and turn to medium low. Let the rice steam until it cooks up light and fluffy. This will take about 40-45 minutes. This brown rice cooks to an almost white color similar to cream of wheat cereal. Serve in individual bowls letting your family put on their own honey, raisins, cinnamon, nutmeg and milk. This is a very nutritious breakfast. Serve with sliced bananas and/or other fresh fruit. Note: The rice may be cooked whole as you would any other rice and served in the same way.

Variations...

Sprinkle on top of this cereal (or any other cereal) a few spoonfuls of granola.

The Best of Granolas

    6 c. rolled oats (can use any   1 c. nuts (more if you wish,
      combination of rolled grains)   whole or chopped—walnuts,
    ½ to 1 c. wheat germ   cashews, almonds, pecans)
    1 c. unsweetened coconut   ½ c. sunflower seeds

1 c. ribbon coconut
¼ c. sesame seeds
1 t. almond extract (optional)
2 T. vanilla

½ c. vegetable oil
1 c. honey (to taste)
1 c. raisins (or other dried fruit)

Mix grains, nuts, seeds, coconut together thoroughly. Pour oil and honey over mixture and stir well. Spread on lightly-oiled cookie sheet and bake at 300° for 30 minutes or until golden brown. Stir occasionally while baking. When mixture is golden brown, take out and mix in the raisins and any other dried fruit you wish to add, vanilla and almond extract. Put back into oven and bake for another 5-10 minutes. Pour granola into large bowl and drizzle about ½ c. additional honey over the mixture. Stir well and allow to cool. Serve with milk and fresh fruit or eat alone. Store in a tightly sealed container. Refrigerate if kept long. For variety add 1 t. cinnamon and 1 t. nutmeg. This granola is good just to snack on and is nutritionally high in protein and the B vitamins.

Whole-Wheat Pancakes

2 eggs
2 c. whole wheat flour
1½ c. milk (or buttermilk)
4 T. oil

2 T. honey
4 t. baking powder
1 t. salt

Beat eggs until fluffy. Stir in the remaining ingredients until just barely smooth. Spoon about 3 T. batter from large spoon or pour from a pitcher onto electric fry pan and cook until golden brown. Serve with your favorite syrups, freezer jams or honey-butter. This makes about 18-20 pancakes. Note: If you use buttermilk, add 1 t. soda.

Whole-Wheat Waffles

2 c. sifted whole wheat flour	4 eggs (separated)
6 t. baking powder	2½ c. milk
1 t. salt	½ c. melted butter
4 T. honey	

Beat egg yolks, milk, honey and oil. Sift dry ingredients and add to liquid mixture. In a separate bowl beat egg whites. Fold beaten egg whites into the first mixture and bake in a hot waffle iron. Serve with frozen jams or syrups. A favorite of our family is to serve with frozen strawberry jam topped with sour cream or whipped cream cheese.

Variation...

You may substitute buttermilk for the milk and add 1 t. soda for a more deluxe waffle.

Michael's Weekend Breakfast Egg Special

4 beaten eggs	¼ c. chopped turkey/chicken
¼ c. milk	and/or ham (use one or all)
¼ t. salt	2 t. finely chopped green pepper
1/8 t. freshly ground pepper	(red pepper if wish)
¼ t. baking powder	1 t. finely chopped onion
¼ c. grated cheese	

Heat fry pan to medium. Mix all the above ingredients with exception of cheese. Cook until almost done, (5 minutes) and add most of

grated cheese. Stir into egg mixture. When eggs are finished cooking, warm two flour tortillas and place cooked eggs on. Roll up and sprinkle remaining cheese on top. Serve with salsa.

Cakes, Cookies, Bars, Ice Cream, Yogurt & Deserts

Carrot Cake

2 c. raw grated carrots
3 c. whole wheat flour
2 c. brown sugar
1 ¼ c. vegetable oil
1½ c. chopped walnuts
½ c. coconut

1 small can crushed pineapple
3 eggs (well beaten)
2 T. grated orange peel
2 t. soda
2 t. vanilla
½ t. salt
1 t. cinnamon

Mix all dry ingredients together and add carrots, oil, pineapple and eggs. Add nuts and stir well. Bake in large flat oiled pan or a tube pan at 350° for 45 minutes to 1 hour (depending upon your oven). When cool, serve with whipped cream or frosting.

Frosting: (Mix all ingredients well and frost.)
1 lb. powdered sugar 1 t. lemon juice
1 cube margarine 1 t. vanilla
1 6 oz. cream cheese ¼ t. almond extract

Whole Wheat Party Cake

1½ c. brown sugar
6 eggs (separated)
½ c. water
1 t. vanilla
1 t. lemon juice

½ t. almond extract
1½ c. whole wheat flour
¼ t. salt
1 t. cream of tartar

Beat until thick and creamy; egg yolks, sugar, water, vanilla, lemon juice and almond extract. Sift dry ingredients and add gradually to first mixture. In separate bowl beat egg whites and cream of tartar until stiff peaks form. Fold beaten egg whites into flour mixture and bake in ungreased tube pan for 1 hour at 325°. Invert pan and cool before removing.

Variations...

> Serve with fresh sliced strawberries and whipped cream. To do this, slice the cake in half (top half and bottom half) so that you have two full rings. Do this with a saw knife. Spread the strawberry slices around whole bottom cake and then replace the top cake. Spread more strawberries on top and frost the whole cake with whipped cream. Put into the freezer to set up for about 1-2 hours before serving. (We use this kind of cake for birthdays and put candles on top just before serving.)
>
> This cake can also be used with lemon sauce placed between the two layers and on top and then frosted with lemon frosting. You can also bake on a large cookie sheet and frost with any kind of frosting. Be creative. Try your own ideas.

Fresh Apple Cake

4 c. diced apples	1 t. vanilla
2 c. brown sugar	2 c. whole wheat flour
½ c. oil	2 t. soda
2 beaten eggs	2 t. cinnamon
1 c. chopped nuts	1 t. salt

Mix all ingredients together. Pour mixture into greased and floured 9x13 pan and bake at 350° for 50-60 minutes. This cake is good served hot with whipped cream, or as a pudding with a caramel sauce and whipped cream on top, or cooled with a cream cheese frosting.

Whole Wheat Carob Cake

1 c. brown sugar	2 t. baking soda
1 c. light mayonnaise	1 pinch salt
5 T. carob powder	2 t. vanilla
2 c. whole wheat flour	1 c. hot water

Cream sugar and mayonnaise together. Mix hot water, carob, soda and add to sugar mixture. Add flour, salt and vanilla. Beat with beaters until smooth and creamy. Pour into greased baking dish (9x12) and bake at 350° for 25-30 minutes. Cool and frost with a carob (3 T.), margarine, vanilla, and powdered sugar frosting. Sprinkle with crushed nuts. Try this—you will be amazed at the taste.

Tangerine or Orange Chiffon Cake

5 tangerines or 3 large oranges	½ c. canola or vegetable oil
2 1/4 c. flour (whole wheat or unbleached white)	5 large egg yolks
	7 large egg whites
1 T. baking powder	½ t. cream of tartar
¾ t. salt	tangerine glaze
1½ c. sugar	

1. Preheat oven to 325° Grate 4 t. peel and squeeze ¾ c. juice from tangerines or oranges. In large bowl combine sugar, oil, egg yolks and beat until creamy and fluffy. Add peel, and juice and beat until smooth.
2. In another bowl combine flour, baking powder, salt and 1 c. sugar. Add the dry ingredients to the first mixture.
3. In another large bowl, with mixer at high speed, beat egg whites and cream of tartar to soft peaks. Continue beating at a high speed and gradually sprinkle in ½ c. sugar until whites are stiff. Fold 1/3 of beaten whites into yolk mixture; then fold in remaining whites.
4. Pour batter into ungreased 10-inch tube or angel food cake pan

and bake 1 hour and 15 minutes or until the top of the cake springs back when touched. Invert cake in pan and cool.

5. Mix tangerine glaze and spread over top of cake and let drizzle down the sides of the cake. Let stand for 1 hour.

Makes 16 servings and takes about 30 minutes preparation time.

Tangerine/Orange Glaze

Mix with beaters 1 c. confectioners' sugar, 1 t. grated tangerine or orange peel, and ¼ tangerine or orange juice until glaze is spreadable. (Sometimes I add more tangerine or orange juice and 2-3 t. of lemon juice for a tarter taste. (I found this recipe in a woman's magazine and made a few changes to suit our family taste and had to add it because this cake is so good—and I really mean it.)

Lemon-Poppyseed Pound Cake

2 c. unbleached white flour (whole wheat can be used)	¾ c. softened margarine or butter
2 T. poppyseeds	1½ c. plus 1/3 c. sugar
½ t. baking powder	4 large eggs
¼ t. baking soda	1 t. vanilla extract
¼ t. salt	½ c. sour cream
2 lemons	

Preheat oven to 325°. Grease and flour 9x5 metal loaf pan. In medium bowl, combine first 5 ingredients. Grate 1 T. peel and squeeze 3 T. juice from lemons.

In large bowl, mixing at low speed, beat margarine with 1½ c. sugar until blended. Continue beating at high speed until light, about 5 minutes. Add eggs, 1 at a time, beating well after each addition. Beat in lemon peel and vanilla. Beating at a low speed, alternately add flour mixture and sour cream, beginning and ending with flour mixture. Spoon batter into pan and bake 1 hour 20 minutes or until toothpick inserted in cake comes out clean.

Cool cake in pan on wire rack for 10 minutes. Remove from pan. Mix lemon juice and 1/3 c. sugar; brush over top and sides of warm cake. Cool and serve.

Serves 16. (I also found this recipe in a woman's magazine and have made a few changes and incorporated it into our family's meals.)

Mrs. A's Fantastic Cookies I

2 c. white sugar	1 t. soda
2 c. brown sugar	2 t. baking powder
4 eggs	¼ t. salt (optional)
½ c. cream or canned milk	4½ c. flour (half whole wheat/
1 lb. butter or butter-	half white or all whole wheat)
flavored margarine	5 c. oatmeal (quick or regular)
½ t. almond extract	1 pkg. carob or chocolate chips
1 t. vanilla	1 pkg. butterscotch chips (opt.)
2 c. chopped nuts	1 pkg. Reeses Pieces (optional)
2 c. raisins	

Cream butter, sugar, eggs, vanilla, almond extract until fluffy. Add flour and other dry ingredients, oats last. Stir well and add nuts. (I usually divide the dough in half and stir raisins into one half and either carob or chocolate chips, butterscotch chips or Reeses Pieces into the other half. You can put a combination mixture of the chips and/or Reeses Pieces or just one kind for the half batch of dough.) Roll dough into golf-size balls and mash down with a fork onto greased cookie sheet. Bake at 400° for 6-8 minutes. DO NOT OVER BAKE. Take out of oven and let cookies cool on cookie sheet while they finish baking. When cooled, put cookies on tray. (If dough seems a little stiff, work a little more cream into mixture.)

Mrs. A's Fantastic Cookies II

(1)
1 lb. butter/margarine
2 c. brown sugar
2 c. white sugar
4 eggs
1 t. vanilla
4 T. cream or milk

(2)
2 c. whole wheat flour
2 c. unbleached white flour
½-1 t. salt
2 t. baking soda
2 t. baking powder

(3)
4 c. oatmeal (quick or regular)
2 c. chopped walnuts
1 pkg. carob/choc. chips
1 pkg. peanut butter or butterscotch chips
1 pkg. Reeses Pieces
1 c. chopped almond bark or white choc.
2-3 c. raisins

(1) Cream until fluffy.
(2) Sift and mix with #(1). (Often I just use 4 c. of whole wheat flour).
(3) Add any, part or all of these. (I always add nuts, then divide the batter into halves and add the raisins to one half and to the other half add carob chips, chopped almond bark, and peanut butter chips.) I like to use the Reeses Pieces in the fall and for Halloween.
(4) Bake on oiled cookie sheet at 350° for 8-10 minutes. You can use a teaspoon to drop the cookie dough onto the cookie sheet or use a floured ice cream scoop if you want a larger cookie. DO NOT OVER-BAKE. Take the cookie sheet from the oven and let the cookies cool on the cookie sheet while they finish baking. When cooled, place cookies on serving tray.

Chewy Oatmeal Cookies

¾ c. oil
1½ c. brown sugar
1 egg
¼ c. water
1 t. vanilla
¼ t. almond extract

1 c. whole wheat flour
½ t. salt
½ t. soda
1 t. cinnamon
½ c. chopped nuts
3 c. oatmeal (quick or regular)
1 c. raisins

Cream oil, sugar, egg, water and flavorings. Sift dry ingredients and add to first mixture. Stir in oats and drop by teaspoon onto greased cookie sheet. Bake 12-15 minutes in a 350° oven. These cookies are good with butterscotch chips added and the raisins and cinnamon deleted. For a more crisp cookie, add 1 c. coconut with the oatmeal (leaving out raisins and cinnamon).

Whole Wheat Cookies

1½-1¾ c. whole wheat flour
½ t. baking soda
½ t. salt
½ c. vegetable oil
6 T. granulated sugar
1 egg

6 T. brown sugar
½ t. vanilla
¼ t. water
½ c. chopped nuts
½ c. carob, chocolate or
butterscotch chips

Sift all dry ingredients and set aside. Blend butter, sugars, vanilla and water. Beat in egg and mix well. Add the dry ingredients, nuts and chips. Drop by half-teaspoon on greased cookie sheet. Bake at 375° for 10-12 minutes. If cookies are turning out too flat, add a little more flour. If too stiff, add a little less flour. All depends on humidity & weather.

Whole Wheat Macaroons

2 egg whites	2 T. whole wheat flour
dash of salt	2 c. grated or shredded coconut
½ c. brown sugar	

Beat egg whites with dash of salt in small bowl until foamy. Add sugar about 1 tablespoon at a time, beating at high speed until stiff peaks form. Fold in flour, then blend in the coconut. Measure and drop from teaspoon 2 inches apart onto greased baking sheet. Bake at 375° about 12 minutes. This makes 12 cookies more or less. Recipe can be doubled or tripled.

Jumbo Raisin Cookies

1 c. water	½ t. cinnamon
2 c. raisins	¼ t. nutmeg
1 c. shortening	½ t. allspice
2 c. brown sugar	1½ t. salt
1 t. vanilla	2 t. soda
3 eggs	2 t. baking powder
4 c. whole wheat flour	1 c. chopped nuts

In sauce pan bring water to boil and add 2 c. raisins. Set aside to cool. In a large bowl cream shortening, sugar and vanilla. Add this mixture to cooled raisins, which have been put into large mixing bowl. Add eggs and beat well. Sift all the dry ingredients and add to the first mixture. Mix well and drop from spoon. Bake at 350° for 10-15 minutes.

Honey Apple Cookies

½ c. oil or margarine	Mix
¾ c. honey	
1 egg	
1 c. grated raw apples	

2 c. flour (whole wheat)	Add and Mix
1 c. oats, regular	
1 t. soda	
1 t. cinnamon	
½ t. salt	
½ t. nutmeg	
1 c. raisins (or dates or both)	

Drop by spoon on oiled sheet. Bake 350° for 10-12 minutes.

No-bake Cookies

½ c. canned milk	3 c. brown sugar
1 c. butter	3 T. carob powder (omit carob for carmel taste)

Heat the above mixture to boiling and then stir until it thickens and forms a soft ball when put into cold water. Remove from heat and add the following:

3 c. quick or regular rolled oats	½ c. sunflower seeds
1 c. coconut (shredded and/or ribbon)	½ c. raisins (optional)
1 c. chopped nuts (walnut, almond, pecan, cashew or a mixture of all)	1 T. vanilla

Mix well and drop by spoonful onto wax paper. Let cool for ½ hour before serving.

Carob Whole Wheat Brownies

Melt together:
>   10 2/3 T. carob/cocoa powder
>   2/3 c. plus 2 T. butter or margarine (or salad oil)

Beat well:
>   2 c. brown/white sugar, 4 eggs

Sift together:
>   1½ c. whole wheat flour
>   1 t. baking powder
>   1 t. salt

Mix together:
>   carob mixture, sugar mixture, and flour mixture,
>   beating at high speed for 3-5 minutes.

Add:
>   1 c. chopped nut meats
>   2 t. vanilla

Spread on buttered cookie sheet and bake at 300° for 30 minutes, or until toothpick comes out clean. DO NOT OVER BAKE. Frost with carob frosting and sprinkle with finely chopped nuts.

Rachelle's Blondies

Cream together:
>   ¾ c. butter
>   4 eggs
>   2 c. sugar

Beat in:
>   2½ c. + 2 T. flour (white)
>   1 t. coconut extract
>   1 t. vanilla

Bake at 350° for 20-25 minutes in oiled 9x13 pan. Cool and frost with the following mixture:

1½ c. powdered sugar	½ t. almond extract
2 T. butter	½ t. vanilla
2 T. shortening	
1-2 T. milk	

Sprinkle with chopped nuts if desired. Cut and serve.

Carmel Brownies

¼ c. shortening	½ t. salt
1 c. brown sugar	½ t. vanilla
1 egg, beaten	½ c. broken walnuts
¾ c. sifted whole wheat flour	½ package butterscotch chips
1 t. baking powder	

Melt shortening and blend with sugar, cool. Stir in beaten egg and then dry ingredients. Add vanilla and nuts. Bake in 8-inch greased pan for 25 minutes at 350°. Don't over bake. Cut in squares while hot. Dust with powdered sugar.

Quick Bars

1 cube butter, melted	1 c. carob and/or peanut
1 package graham crackers	butter chips
2 c. wide ribbon coconut	1 can Sweetened
1-2 c. pecans (or chopped	Condensed Milk
almonds)	

Put melted butter in 9 x 13 inch pan. Place all other ingredients in layers on top of butter, laying graham crackers on the bottom as a base. Drizzle the condensed milk over the top and bake at 350° for 20-30 minutes. Let it cool slightly and cut into squares while still warm.

Whole Grain Jam Squares

2 c. quick or old-fashioned,   ½ c. chopped nuts
uncooked rolled oats   1 t. cinnamon
1 ¾ c. whole wheat flour   ¾ t. salt
1 c. butter or margarine   ½ t. soda
1 c. firmly packed brown sugar   1 c. any flavor preserves
                                     (I like to use apricot or plum)

Combine all ingredients except preserves in large mixing bowl; beat at a low speed with electric mixer until mixture is crumbly. Reserve 2 c. mixture; press remaining onto the bottom of greased 13x9" pan. Spread preserves evenly over base; sprinkle with reserved mixture. Bake in hot oven (400°) 25-30 minutes or until golden brown. Cool; cut into squares.

Variations...

Omit nuts in oat mixture and add ¼ t. nutmeg and 1/3 t. cloves.
   Substitute 1 c. applesauce, ¾ c. raisins and ½ c. nuts for preserves.

Fruit-Nut Bars

½ c. chopped raisins   ½ c. sunflower seeds
½ c. chopped dates   ¼ c. carob powder
½ c. chopped prunes   ¼ c. honey
½ c. chopped nuts   ½ c. coconut

Mix all ingredients together well. Butter shallow baking dish and line with sunflower seed meal, finely chopped nuts or coconut and spread mixture. Sprinkle with nuts, coconut and chill. Cut into bars.

Yummy Peanut Butter Candy Bars

1 pound margarine
3 pounds powdered sugar
3 c. smooth peanut butter

Mix above ingredients together and roll into small bars. Chill for a couple of hours and then dip in melted chocolate or carob bars.

Nut Crunch

1½ c. Roman Meal (or finely
  ground grain cereal)
1½ c. oatmeal
1 c. dry powdered milk
1 c. peanuts
1 c. raisins

1 c. honey
1 c. peanut butter
½ c. molasses
½ c. sunflower seeds
½ c. chopped or sliced almonds

Mix all ingredients well and form into balls the size of a golf ball. Roll in sesame seeds, coconut, or crushed nuts. (If mixture seems dry, add a little more honey. For variety add 3 T. carob powder.)

Dori's Almond Roca

9 x 13" baking pan
1½ c. almonds (finely chopped)
3 c. grated carob
1 c. butter (or margarine)

½ c. fructose
¼ t. salt
3 T. water
1 T. vanilla

Butter pan and sprinkle on ½ the amount of almonds and carob. In separate pan melt butter, add fructose, water and salt. Cook until reaches crack stage (candy thermometer 350°). Stir constantly. Quickly add vanilla and pour over carob and almonds. Add the rest of carob and almonds on top.

Kristine's Apple Pie Filling

6 quarts blanched, sliced fresh apples	2½ cold water
5½ c. granulated sugar	5 c. apple juice (use water from blanching)
1½ c. clear gel A	¾ c. lemon juice
1 T. cinnamon	1 t. nutmeg

Use quality, firm, crisp apples. Macintosh, Golden Delicious, Johnathan (Empire)

Procedure:

Wash, peel, core apples. Prepare slices ½" wide and place in water containing ascorbic acid to prevent browning. For fresh fruit, place 6 c. at a time into 1 gallon of boiling water. Boil each batch 20 seconds after water returns to boiling. Drain, but keep heated fruit in a covered bowl or pot.

Combine sugar, clear gel, cinnamon, and nutmeg in a large kettle.

Add water and apple juice. Stir and cook on medium high heat until mixture thickens and begins to bubble.

Add lemon juice and boil 1 minute, stirring constantly.

Fold in drained apple slices immediately and fill clean jars with mixture without delay, leaving 1" headspace. Adjust lids and process immediately. Hot pack 35 minutes for pints or quarts. Makes 7 Quarts.

(Kris uses this recipe, which she got from a friend, to make quick apple pies by placing a bottled quart into a previously baked pie crust. She serves the pie with whipped cream or vanilla ice cream.)

Miriam's Peach Cobbler

4 c. fresh peaches	Mix & place in oiled baking dish
dash of salt	
1-2 T. flour	
1-2 T. sugar	
1 egg	Beat these 4 ingredients
½ c. melted butter	

½ c. sugar
½ c. milk

1½ c. flour (white or wheat)   Add to liquid mixture
½ t. salt
2 t. baking powder
½ t. nutmeg

Spoon over peaches and bake at 425° for 25 minutes. Cover with foil for the last ten minutes of baking. Cool and serve with one of the following sauces and/or whipped cream.

Sauce 1:
Combine 1 c. sugar, 2 T. corn starch, 2 c. hot water, and bring to boil for 1 minute, until mixture thickens. Add 4 T. butter and 2 t. vanilla, 2 t. of lemon juice, 1 T. grated lemon rind can be added, or 2 t. nutmeg.

Sauce 2:
Combine 1 T. corn starch, 1/3 c. sugar, 2 T. vanilla, dash of salt, 1 or 2 t. nutmeg, 1 c. water and 2 T. butter. Bring to a boil and thicken stirring continually until thick. (4 minutes) Pour either of these sauces over cake after removing from oven. Serve the cake warm and with fresh whipped cream. (This is a pleaser.)

Frozen Banana Milk Shake

Fill blender ½ full of milk.* Add 4 or more frozen bananas, 1 t. vanilla, honey to taste, 1 T. oil and blend until smooth. You may add carob or cocoa powder (1-3 T.), or frozen strawberries, raspberries, etc. Fresh peaches are also good to add to the frozen banana mixture. Be creative and try your own combinations. This is a good pick-up when kids come home from school.
    *If you wish, add less milk and more fruit.

Banana Delight

5 T. natural oil—olive, soy, safflower, sunflower, etc.
½ lemon, juiced fresh
½ c. natural, unsweetened macaroon coconut (granulated)
1 banana, sliced

Place oil in serving dish. Add lemon juice. Add coconut and sliced banana. Stir and serve immediately. Serves 2-3. Adjust amount of ingredients to suit taste.

Fruit Friz

In a blender put 1 12-oz. can orange juice concentrate, 3-5 ripe bananas, fresh or bottled apricots (if using bottled, put juice and all) and either crushed pineapple (15 or 20 oz. can) or fill with pineapple juice. Pour part of liquid out into separate container and continue adding fruits and juices until you have two blenders full of mixed liquid. Pour into ice cube trays and freeze. When frozen, put ice cubes through a food processor or blender to mix into a soft ice-cream-like consistency. I use my Champion Juicer to do this. Then put back into the freezer until you serve it. You may also pour the whole mixture into a baking dish and freeze. When frozen, chop into chunks and serve either plain or with 7-Up.

Mignonne's Great Tasting and Good For You Smoothies

Combine all the ingredients in a blender and mix until smooth. These are very refreshing and will make a hit with your family.

Berry Delicious Smoothie

2 c. apple berry juice
½ c. nonfat berry yogurt
½ c. crushed ice

½ c. blueberries, raspberries,
   or blackberries (frozen)

Classic Smoothie

¾ c. nonfat plain yogurt
¾ c. orange juice
½ t. vanilla extract
1 large banana

¾ c. strawberries
2 T. honey
1 c. crushed ice

Cool Island Dream

1 fresh pineapple cut into chunks
1 fresh mango cut into cubes
1 T. raw sugar or honey

¼ c. pineapple juice
1/3 c. soy milk
1 c. crushed ice

Fruit Smoothie

1½ c. orange juice
½ c. cubed cantaloupe
1 T. frozen apple juice
  concentrate

½ banana
1 t. vanilla extract
1 t. coconut extract
¼ c. nonfat plain yogurt

Rachelle's Mango/Guava Drink with Lime Zest

1 pound frozen mango
1 c. frozen guava concentrate
1 c. sour cream (non-fat)

2 c. skim milk
¼ c. sugar

Puree mango; add rest of ingredients and puree for a few minutes until smooth. Chill several hours and serve with dollop of sour cream, sliced berries and grated lime zest. (I have made this with frozen peaches or nectarines. It is very good and I use it as a thick drink with a meal or as a desert.)

Homemade Vanilla Ice Cream

4 eggs (8 for more creamy)	4 c. heavy cream
2½ c. sugar	4½ t. vanilla
5 c. milk	½ t. salt

Add sugar gradually to beaten eggs. Continue to beat mixture until very stiff. Add remaining ingredients and mix thoroughly. Pour into can and freeze as directed according to your freezer directions.

Variations...
   • *Strawberry Ice Cream:* Substitute 3 cups of fresh mashed straw-
     berries for 3 of the cups of milk. Add a little red food coloring, if
     you wish, and follow the rest of the directions.
   • *Maple Nut Ice Cream:* Substitute brown sugar for the sugar, add
     1 c. chopped walnuts and 1 t. of maple flavoring in addition to
     the vanilla. (Sometimes, I just use brown sugar as the flavoring.)

Nathan's Quick Dessert

1 quart vanilla ice cream	1 c. fresh raspberries
1 c. fresh blueberries	1 c. fresh strawberries

Wash and drain berries. Slice strawberries and mix with raspberries and blueberries. Scoop ice cream into dish and spoon on the
berries. Serve with a cookie.

Homemade Yogurt

Blend:
   2 c. water
   1½ c. powdered skim milk
   3 T. plain yogurt (with live cultures)

Add:
    1 quart water
    1 large can evaporated milk

Mix all ingredients well and fill in 8 glasses holding 8 ounces each or 4 pint jars. Place in a yogurt maker or a pan of warm water coming to the brim of the glasses or jars. Cover the pan and place in the oven keeping the temperature 105°-120° for 3 hours or until it becomes the texture of pudding.

This yogurt will keep in the refrigerator for a week or more, the bacterial qualities improving up to eight days after being made. Some ways of serving yogurt are plain or topped with fresh or frozen berries, homemade jams, pineapple, fresh fruits or puree, such as apricot, plum, peach, etc.

Yogurt can be used in salad dressing, in place of sour cream on potatoes, made into ice creams or sherbets. It can be used as you would in making sundaes or banana splits. Be creative and make up your own combinations.

Gelatin Yogurt

2 envelopes unflavored gelatin   2/3 c. instant nonfat dry milk
4 T. cold water   8 c. low-fat or skim milk
6 T. plain yogurt start (room temperature)

Soften gelatin in cold water for 5 minutes. Pour 2 c. of low-fat milk into another bowl. Add dry milk and stir until dissolved. Pour remaining 6 c. of milk, the dissolved dry milk, and the softened gelatin into a 4-quart pan which has been rinsed with warm water. Mix well and heat on low until temperature reaches between 190°-210°. Then remove and cool to 110° and remove film from surface.

In a small bowl, stir yogurt until creamy and then mix 2/3 c. warm milk mixture into the yogurt. Blend until smooth and then stir yogurt-milk mixture into the remaining milk. Mix well and pour into 6 pint jars. Place in a large pan of warm water coming to the brim of the jar and cover the pan with a lid. Place in oven and keep at a constant temperature of 110° for three to five hours. Refrigerate four to six hours before serving.

Note: If you have a small family, you may wish to divide the recipe in half.

Flavored Yogurt

Sundae-Style...
Place your own flavorings in the bottom of small containers. (These can be your frozen berry jams, peach, apricot, pineapple, plum, etc., or your cooked preserves. You may want to mix more than one flavoring. Be creative.)

Add enough warm milk yogurt mixture to fill cups or jars to about ½ inch from the top.

Place in yogurt maker or a large pan filled with warm water, the water coming to the neck of the jar. Cover and let the yogurt incubate 3-5 hours.

Swiss-Style...
Put 1 T. of any flavor of thick preserves into an 8-ounce container and add warm milk with yogurt starter. Mix well and let incubate for 3 to 5 hours. If you use the 16-ounce jars, put in 2 T. of flavoring.

Flavor Ideas...
Applesauce, Apricot, Banana, Blueberry, Cherry, Lemon, Orange, Peach, Pineapple-Coconut, Raspberry, Strawberry, Vanilla.

Commercial yogurt is heavy on sugar, so you may wish to use just the fruit or merely add a teaspoon of honey to the fruit if you are not using preserves. For vanilla you should use 1 t. vanilla extract to 2 or 3 t. of sugar. Or, there are recipes for vanilla yogurt if you wish the whole batch to be vanilla.

Vanilla Yogurt

6 c. warm water (120°)	1 c. sweetened condensed milk
2 c. instant nonfat dry milk	½ c. plain yogurt (room temp.)
1 t. vanilla extract (you may wish to use more—suit your taste)	

Mix ingredients in a bowl. Use electric mixer on a low speed. Pour into individual containers or a 1½ quart container. Cover and incubate 3-4 hours. If you do not use a yogurt maker, place in a pan of warm water and put in oven at 110°. When pudding-like, refrigerate for six hours. This is a good dessert eaten plain or served with a fruit sauce over it, topped with nuts or your own homemade granola.

Frozen Strawberry Yogurt

1 quart fresh strawberries	1½ c. sugar
1 quart plain yogurt	1 t. vanilla

Wash strawberries and blend until almost smooth. In a large bowl, stir yogurt until smooth. Stir in sugar and vanilla. Next stir in pureed berries and blend well. Pour into ice cream canister and freeze in ice cream maker according to the manufacturer's directions. Makes 2½ quarts. Note: You can substitute any kind of fruit for the strawberries.

Creamy Frozen-Strawberry Yogurt

1 6-oz. pkg. strawberry-flavored gelatin	1 qt. fresh strawberries
1½ c. sugar or honey	4 c. plain yogurt
2 c. water	2 c. whipping cream

Combine gelatin and sugar in large saucepan, add water and stir over medium heat until gelatin is dissolved. Then set aside. Wash and puree berries in a blender and stir into the gelatin mixture. In a separate large bowl, stir yogurt. Stir in strawberry mixture and whipping cream. Pour into ice cream canister and freeze in the ice cream maker according to the directions of the manufacturer. Makes about 1 gallon.

Frozen Yogurt Popcicles

> 4 c. of any berry-flavored or plain yogurt
> 4 c. fresh or thawed frozen berries
> 4 T. of the same berry preserves

Blend all ingredients in a blender for about two minutes. Pour into twelve 5-ounce paper cups. Freeze until partially firm (about 30 minutes). Place wooden stick in center of each cup. Freeze until hard. To serve, peel off the paper cup.

Suggested Flavors:

Strawberry, Raspberry, Blueberry Pineapple, Cherry

Variations...

Instead of the 4 c. of fresh or frozen fruit and preserves, you may blend 1 6-oz. can frozen orange, lemon or lime concentrate, partially thawed, into the flavored or plain yogurt. (Kids love these treats.)

SOUP, SALAD, SANDWICHES

French Onion Soup

6-8 large onions	6 beef bouillon cubes and/or
1 cube butter or margarine	2 T. beef stock base
8 c. water	1 t. Worcestershire Sauce

Slice onions very thin. Sauté in 1 cube butter until tender and almost browning stage. Add 8 c. water and bouillon cubes and/or beef stock base. (I usually add cubes and then taste. If I need more flavor, I add 1 T. beef stock base and continue to add 1 at a time until I have the right flavor.) Simmer until the cubes and base are dissolved and add 1 t. Worcestershire sauce. Simmer for 20-30 minutes. Serve with Parmesan cheese or any grated cheese (white or orange) of your choice. Garnish with croutons and chopped parsley. Serves 6-8.

Clam Chowder

1 can 6½ oz. minced clams or any cooked fish	1 c. flour
	1 c. half 'n half cream
1 c. finely chopped onions	1½ t. salt
1 c. finely diced celery	few grains white pepper
2 c. finely diced potatoes	1 cube butter or margarine
1 c. diced carrots	2 T. white vinegar
1 can cream of celery soup	1 can evaporated milk (13 oz.)
1 can cream of chicken soup	

Drain juice from clams and pour over vegetables in large saucepan; add vinegar and enough more water to barely cover. Simmer, covered, over medium heat until barely tender. In meantime, blend in blender the cream, flour and salt. Stir this cream mixture into the cooked vegetables, and bring to a boil, continuing to stir constantly. When mixture thickens, add the cans of cream of celery and cream of chicken soups. Stir until smooth and turn the heat to low. Now stir the can of evaporated milk in, add the pepper and the cube of butter. When the butter has melted, serve garnished with parsley. Serves 8.

Cream of Chicken Soup

1 chicken	Cook; cool and strip meat from bones
3 c. water	
1 c. powdered milk	Blend
1 c. flour	
1 t. salt	
3 diced potatoes	
4 chopped pieces celery	Cook vegetables in chicken
1 chopped onion	broth until tender
4 shredded carrots	
2 cans cream of chicken soup	
1 can evaporated milk	

When vegetables are tender, add the flour and powdered milk mixture and stir constantly bringing to a boil. When thick add 2 cans cream of chicken or cream of celery soup and 1 can evaporated milk and stir until smooth. Stir all the time the milk mixture is thickening or it will burn. Next add big chunks of chicken to the thickened mixture and garnish with fresh parsley and grated cheese. Just before serving add a big chunk of butter.

Variation...

You can use the same idea and use broccoli in place of the chicken. Also use same idea for cream of potato soup, leaving out chicken and carrots.

Lentil Soup

1 c. dry lentils	1 chopped onion
5 c. water	2 c. grated carrots
4 each beef & chicken bouillon	½ c. chopped celery
dash of garlic powder	

Place in pressure cooker or presto cooker and cook until tender, approximately 3 hours. (Slow cooker or Crock-pot approx. 6-7 hrs.) When ready to serve put ¼ cube butter in soup and garnish with chopped parsley. This soup is good served with hot homemade whole wheat bread sticks. You may also add chopped, cooked bacon if you wish.

The Greatest Beef Stew

1 lb beef stew meat (small cube)	1 c. frozen corn
2 onions, chopped	4-6 beef bouillon cubes
3 peeled & sliced carrots	3 c. water
3 peeled and cubed potatoes	¼ c. chopped parsley
2 stocks celery, chopped	5 T. cornstarch
2 unpeeled & sliced zucchini	½ c. cold water
1 c. frozen green peas	

Seasonings to your taste:

salt & pepper	¼ t. sweet basil
garlic salt	onion salt
celery salt	1/8 t. chili powder
½ t. paprika	

Brown meat and one of the chopped onions in a small amount of oil until tender. Add all chopped vegetables (carrots, potatoes, onion, celery, zucchini), bouillon cubes, 3 c. water and all the seasonings, and simmer until the vegetables are just barely tender. Mix the 5 T. of cornstarch into the ½ c. cold water and stir cornstarch mixture into the

...ixture. Turn the heat down to low immediately ...ckened and add the frozen peas and corn. Let it ...utes while frozen vegetables heat through. Serve ...the color of the peas is bright green and the corn brign... ....before serving, sprinkle top with chopped parsley.

Note:

This stew is a meal in itself and is good served with hot homemade whole wheat rolls or bread and honey-butter or your own preserves or jams.

If you have leftover roast of any kind, you may substitute for the stew meat following the same directions but not cooking as long.

Taco Salad

1 pound hamburger	½ pound grated cheese
1 medium onion, chopped	2 chopped tomatoes
1 pkg. taco seasoning or	3 chopped green onions
make your own	1 can kidney beans
1 head lettuce (broken)	1 pkg. corn chips
1 large avocado	

Brown together hamburger, onion and taco seasoning; simmer 15-20 minutes. Combine in a large bowl; lettuce, avocado, cheese, tomatoes, green onions, kidney beans, and corn chips. Just before serving, add hamburger mixture and toss. Serve plain or with French or buttermilk dressing stirred into the salad at the last minute. For additional nutrition add ½ c. each of alfalfa and mung bean sprouts. To extend hamburger, add mashed pinto beans, if you wish.

Super Taco Salad

2 c. mashed refried beans, or	2 chopped fresh tomatoes
drained chili beans	1 peeled, sliced avocado
1½ c. green chili salsa, or	(dip in lemon juice)

tomato salsa
4 T. vegetable oil
1 t. ground cumin
6 c. shredded lettuce

½ c. sliced ripe olives
1 c. shredded cheddar cheese
2 c. tortilla chips

Combine salsa, oil and cumin in a small bowl and beat vigorously. Arrange lettuce, beans, tomatoes, avocado and olives in a large salad bowl, in that order. Add cheese and chips in the salad just before serving. Pour salsa over the salad and serve immediately. Serves 6.

Turkey Salad Supreme

3 c. julienne strips cooked
   turkey breast
1 c. narrow strips of ham
2 medium tomatoes
1 large avocado, peeled
3 hard cooked eggs
½ pound crisp cooked bacon
½ c. finely grated cheddar
   cheese

2 T. finely chopped chives
1 medium head lettuce
1 small bunch red lettuce
1 medium head romaine lettuce
½ c. chopped olives
½ c. sliced radishes
1 chopped cucumber
1 c. French dressing (or Italian)

Cut turkey breast into julienne strips. Chop tomatoes, avocado, eggs, cucumber and bacon very fine. In a large salad bowl spread layers of broken lettuce putting the red lettuce leaves on the bottom and sides of the bowl as a decoration. Heap the lettuce slightly in the center. Arrange the turkey, ham, tomatoes, avocado, eggs, bacon, cheese and chives in rows contrasting the colors over the top of the greens. Serve, sprinkling part of the dressing across only one end at a time, tossing lightly and serving from that section. Makes 8-10 large servings.

Miriam's Grape Chicken Almond Salad

1 c. grapes (green or red)
1 can mandrin oranges
½ slivered or sliced almonds
1 c. chopped celery
1/3 c. light mayonaise

3 c. chopped cooked
chicken breasts
1 t. salt
2 T. lemon juice

Put into bowl grapes, drained oranges, almonds, celery and chicken. Sprinkle salt over the mixture as well as lemon juice, and mix. Mix into these ingredients the mayonaise and serve on washed lettuce leaves. (This is a favorite salad and I add it to this book because of its easy preparation and because everyone loves it.)

Rachelle's Herb Garden Tomatoes

6 diced garden tomatoes
1 T. fresh chopped cilantro

1 garlic clove pressed
sugar, salt, and pepper to taste

Mix all ingredients together and serve on toasted French bread or toasted sour dough bread and a slice of Swiss cheese.

Rachelle's Spinich Salad I

½ pound fried, well-drained,
   chopped bacon
1 pound large curd cottage
   cheese
¾ pound grated Swiss Cheese

1 bunch or bag washed and
   dried spinich
1 head iceberg lettuce
1 head romain lettuce

Dressing:
1½ T. poppy seeds
¾ c. white vinegar

1 chopped red onion
Blend all ingredients except

1½ t. white diced onion
1½ c. canola oil
½ t. salt
¾ t. dry mustard
¾ pound sliced mushrooms

mushrooms and red onion together. Add mushrooms and onion in dressing and marinate in refrigerator overnight. Place greens, cheeses and bacon in bowl and pour dressing on and serve.

Rachelle's Spinich Salad II

1 t. poppy seeds
1 c. vegetable oil
½ c. sugar
1 t. minced onion
½ t. dry mustard
1 t. salt
2 bags washed spinich
1 c. grated Swiss cheese
¼ c. minced, cooked bacon
1/3 c. chopped green onions
1/3 c. sliced mushrooms

Optional 1-2 bags mixed greens mandrin oranges, red grapefruit, peanuts or cashews, avacado

Mix in a container the dressing of poppy seeds, oil, sugar, onion, mustard, and salt. Place the remainder of the ingredients in a large bowl and toss. Pour dressing over the salad and serve immediately.

Jennifer's Orange Almond Salad

1 head red or green leaf lettuce (or ½ of each)
1 c. fresh sliced mushrooms
1 sliced red onion
1 11-oz. can drained mandrin oranges
1 c. sliced almonds
3 T. sugar

Place almonds and sugar in fry pan and constantly stir until sugar turns golden brown and coats the almonds. Set aside to cool. Meanwhile, mix the following for the dressing:

½ c. olive oil	2 T. sugar
1/3 c. fresh orange juice	2 T. apple cider vinegar
½ t. grated orange peel	1 T. dry Italian salad dressing powder mix

Place lettuce, mushrooms, onion, oranges and almonds in bowl and pour dressing mixture over salad. Toss and serve.

Fresh Fruit Salad

Cut, chop or slice into a mixing bowl 2 apples, 2 oranges, 2 bananas, 2 kiwi, 1 c. well-drained pineapple, and 1 or 2 c. of red and/or green grapes. Gently stir in 1-2 c. lemon yogurt. Pour mixture into pretty bowl and sprinkle with unsweetened coconut. Sprinkle with pomegranate seeds or dried cranberries, and slice another kiwi on top. The lemon yogurt keeps the fruit from turning brown and this salad is not only pretty to the eye, but a taste pleaser.

Yogurt Salad Dressing

2 c. plain yogurt	½ t. salt
6 T. vegetable salad oil	¼ t. garlic powder
4 T. grated onion	½ t. white pepper
4 t. fresh chopped parsley	1/8 t. ground oregano (optional)
2 T. white vinegar	

Put yogurt, oil, vinegar, onion, parsley, oregano, salt, garlic powder and white pepper in a blender and blend on high for about 3 minutes or until smooth and creamy. Place in a jar and refrigerate for about 2 hours before serving. Makes about 3 cups.

Variations...

Put all the ingredients in with the exception of the salt, garlic powder, oregano, and pepper. Replace these with 1-2 t. of Spike, which is a salt-substitute seasoning containing herbs and vegetables. I like to use the plain yogurt with Spike for salad dressing without the vinegar and oil. Yogurt and Spike are also good on baked potatoes.

Tuna Salad Spread

1 can well-drained tuna	6 T. mung bean sprouts or
2-3 T. mayonnaise	alfalfa sprouts
1 t. mustard	1 c. shredded lettuce

Mix all together and spread on white or whole wheat buttered bread. If you wish, leave the lettuce out and place it on top of the spread.

Roast Beef Sandwich Spread

If you have some leftover roast, grind in meat grinder about 1 pound of the cooked roast. Put into the ground meat 4-6 T. mayonnaise, 1 t. mustard, 2 T. chopped dill pickle or dill pickle relish and mix well. Spread this mixture onto the buttered bread and place a generous slice of lettuce on the mixture. This is good on whole wheat bread or white bread and for variety you can put sliced tomatoes and/or sprouts on it also. You may wish to grate cheese on the sandwich.

Cream Cheese Sandwich Filling

1 small package cream cheese

3 T. chopped dates
3 T. finely chopped celery
Mix together well and spread on fruit bread.

Variation...

Add well-drained crushed pineapple to cream cheese filling.

Apple Sandwich

Wash and polish an apple. The bigger the better. Carefully remove the center with apple corer. Cut crosswise into 5 or 6 slices, about ½ inch thick. Add mixture of peanut butter and honey on each slice; sprinkle with raisins and nuts and stack back together just as the slices came apart.

Pocket Bread Sandwich Filling

1 medium head cabbage, chopped fine	¾ c. chopped mushrooms
1 medium chopped avocado	2 t. Spike*
1-2 c. alfalfa sprouts	½ c. low calorie or canola mayonnaise
½-¾ c. sunflower seeds	Sliced tomatoes
Slices Swiss or Monterey Jack Cheese	

Combine chopped cabbage, avocado, sprouts, seeds, mushrooms, Spike and mayonnaise together. Put into pocket bread and put a slice of tomato and a slice of cheese in the bread on the filling.

*Spike is a vegetable seasoning which you can get at health food stores or in some grocery stores. You may wish to use more Spike or less depending upon your taste. Experiment. This filling has no meat in and yet it gives the effect of meat. This filling can also be used as a salad or served on whole wheat crackers. Try it, you'll like it. (It may be best not to reveal the ingredients until your family has enjoyed its delicious taste.)

MAIN DISHES

Chicken Fajitas Ole

1 c. cracked wheat (sift out
    fine flour) simmered in
    3 c. water and 4 t. chicken
    bouillon for 20 minutes
    (burns easily)
¼ c. water
1 onion, chopped
salt to taste
garlic powder to taste
1 t. cumin
1 t. chili powder
1 pkg. 12 flour tortillas

2 tomatoes, chopped
2 green peppers, chopped
1 4-oz. can green chilies, chopped
½ c. chopped olives
¼ t. black pepper
¼ t. paprika
2 c. grated mild cheese
2 T. oil
¼ c. chopped green onions
¼ c. chopped parsley
3 stalks celery, chopped
1 c. cooked chicken, chopped

Heat 2 T. oil in wok or fry pan. Sauté green pepper, onion and celery. Add cooked cracked wheat, chicken, and all spices and stir fry. (Taco seasoning may be used instead of the individual spices.) Add tomatoes, green chilies and olives. Toss for a few minutes. Add ¼ c. water and turn heat down to medium low and cook 3-4 minutes. Spoon onto flour tortillas, sprinkle with cheese and roll. Place into a baking dish. Sprinkle with green onion and parsley and the remainder of the cheese and bake in low oven at 300° for 15 minutes. It is good to cover the baking dish with foil so the tortillas won't. dry out. Serve with picante or nacho sauce.

Pinto Bean Dip

2 c. raw pinto beans
1 large onion (chopped)
1-2 c. grated cheese
salt to taste

¼ t. garlic salt
1 t. chili powder
½ t. cumin
3 T. bacon bits

Cook beans and chopped onion in 5 or 6 c. of water until the beans are tender (approximately 4-5 hours). When water has cooked out of beans, add flavors and mash with a potato masher or blend in a blender. Add 1 T. butter and 1 c. of the cheese—stirring into the bean mixture. You may add a few drops of hot sauce to taste. Sprinkle the other cup of cheese on top. Serve with nacho chips. (Taco seasoning can be used instead of the spices.)

Frijoles Picante (Beans)

3 c. dry pinto beans   ½ cube margarine
10 c. water   1 1/3 c. salsa/picante sauce, mild
1 medium onion, chopped   1 can chopped green mild chilies
1 pkg. or 3 t. taco seasoning mix   1 small can olives, chopped
   (1 ¼ oz.)   3 green onions, chopped
2 t. salt   1 pkg. nacho chips, 16 oz.
3 c. mild cheddar cheese, grated

Place washed pinto beans, chopped onion and water into a large Crock-pot and cook on high until beans are very tender and there is very little water left. This takes about 5-6 hours. (If you wish to cook beans faster, do so in a pressure cooker for about 1½ hours.) When beans are cooked, place them along with the remaining liquid into a blender. Make a bean puree by blending on medium speed until smooth, stopping occasionally to scrape down the sides. Blend 1/3 of the beans at a time. When blending the last 1/3 of the beans, place the following into the blender along with the beans: taco seasoning mix, salt, margarine, salsa or picante sauce, chopped green mild chilies, and 2 c. of the grated cheese. Blend until the puree has a very smooth consistency. Place all the bean puree back into the Crock-pot and mix very well. Sprinkle the remaining cup of grated cheese, the green onions, and the chopped olives on top of the bean mixture in the order given. Turn the Crock-pot on low and cover with lid. When the cheese has melted (about 15 minutes), serve with nacho chips and picante sauce, placed in separate bowls. Serves 12 people.

Festive Taco Dip Supreme

Cut into wedge shapes 12 corn
   tortillas
4 c. shredded or diced chicken
1 can whole green chilis
2 cans chopped green chilis
1 can chopped olives
4 chopped green onions
1½ c. cheese (orange or white)

1 c. sour cream
2 cans cream of chicken soup
1 can Mexican tomatoes
1 t. pepper
½ t. salt
1 t. ground cumin
1-2 t. chili powder

Spray Crock-pot with canola oil spray. Layer 1/3 tortillas, chicken, whole chilis. Mix soups, tomatoes, olives, green onions, spices. Pour over tortillas and chicken and chili layers, continuing to do so until 2 inches from top of Crock-pot. Slow cook for 4-5 hours and add cheese last 15 minutes.

Just before serving, top with additional chopped green onions (4), and serve with white nacho corn chips and fresh or canned salsa.

Spanish Fiesta

1-2 pounds hamburger
salt and pepper to taste
1 medium onion
1 pkg. tortillas (already fried)
1 pkg. frozen corn
1 lb. grated cheese

1½ quart tomato juice
1 t. chili powder (+/-)
½ t. pepper
1/8 t. garlic powder
4-6 T. cornstarch
1 t. cumin

Fry hamburger and onion; salt and pepper to taste. Set aside. In sauce pan bring to boil tomato juice, cumin, chili powder, pepper, garlic. In glass (½ c. cold water) stir cornstarch until dissolved. Add cornstarch to tomato mixture and stir until thick. Remove from heat. In baking dish, layer tortillas, hamburger, frozen corn, tomato sauce and cheese in this order. Continue to layer until full. Bake in oven at 325° for 20 minutes or until bubbles and serve with chopped green onion, chopped olives, and corn chips.

Nathan's Chicken Enchiladas

1 pkg enchilada sauce mix	1 8-oz. can tomato cauce
1½ c. water	1 chopped white onion
1-2 c. chopped cooked chicken	2 c. shredded mild cheese
½ c. chopped olives	8 flour tortillas
½ c. chopped green onions	
1 4-oz. can mild diced green chiles	

In a large fry pan combine sauce mix, tomato sauce, and water. Stir and bring to a boil. Reduce heat and simmer for 5 minutes.

In a separate bowl mix chopped onion, cooked chicken, green chiles, and olives. Quickly dip flour tortillas into sauce, coating both sides. Place 3 T. meat, onion, chile mixture down the center of each tortilla and 1 T. of shredded cheese on top. Fold over the tortilla sides and place seam-side down into a large baking dish. Spoon the remaining sauce on to the echniladas. Sprinkle the remaining cheese on top and bake in a 325° oven for 20 minutes or until the sauce is bubbling. Remove from oven and sprinkle green onions on top.

This dish is good served with shredded lettuce, chopped tomatoes, chips, salsa, and sour cream. In addition, serve the pinto bean recipe with this dish.

Enchillada Steak and Everything

Cut into thin strips any kind of beef (such as bottom of the round, top of the round, or any kind of steak meat). You will need 2-4 c. depending upon amount you are serving and how much meat you like. Chop into small pieces 1 green pepper, 1 medium size onion and enough fresh mushrooms to make ½ to 1 c. Chop 2 tomatoes into medium size pieces. Shred 2 c. of mild or white cheese (I use some of each).

In oven, heat at 300° 8 tortillas (medium or large) wrapped very tightly in foil.

Fry the beef strips in butter on medium or low. Cook until brown and then add the onion and pepper. Salt and pepper to taste. Next add the mushrooms and cook a couple of minutes. Now add the tomato chunks and stir while cooking for about 3 minutes. Next add the cheese and stir it into the meat mixture until it melts.

Take tortillas out of oven and while hot butter one side immediately. Then put 2 or 3 T. of the meat mixture and roll the tortilla as you would for enchilladas. Serve immediately.

It's Salsa Time

Get out those chips. It's salsa making time. If you have a family of any size, and especially if you have teenagers, you probably find yourself buying many bottles of salsa sauce over the year's time. By buying a 24-oz. bottle of a famous maker's picante sauce each week paying around $2.75 each, you will have spent $143 for the year on just that one item.

Now consider this. Make your own and the cost would be about $.71 a pint or a little over $.04 an ounce, where the store boughten salsa would cost you nearly three times as much at $.11 an ounce. By making an equal amount of homemade salsa, your cost would be $49.92, and your savings would be $93.08. Yes, it would cost you about six hours to make (three and a half in cooking time), but for a $93 savings, would not that be worth your time. That's $15.51 an hour savings for your work time. However, the greatest advantage to me is that I know what I have put in the salsa—there are no addatives or preservatives, not too much salt, and the taste is superior because I've not skimped on the ingredients. More money can be saved if you plant your own salsa makings in your garden. This is what we do, herbs and all.

With this kind of money savings, you will be able to buy several more cases of other food items which will help build your "home store."

The Greatest Salsa

(I've tried a lot of salsa recipes—but here is the greatest one I know.)

5 large green peppers	2 T. fresh cilantro
3 large red sweet peppers	2 T. fresh oragano
2 large yellow peppers	2 T. fresh sweet basil
2 large white onions	2 T. salt (uniodized)
2 medium red onions	2½ T. cumin
6 cloves garlic	½ t. cayenne
2 red chili peppers	¼ t. paprika
(1 with seeds)	½ bushel roma tomatoes
3 green chili peppers	
(2 with seeds)	
1 or 2 jalapeno for hotter salsa	

Chop the large green, red, and yellow peppers. Chop the red onions. Blend the rest of the ingredients (food processer can be used). Scald the tomatoes in hot water (1-3 minutes) until skins slip off and put into cold water. Core and remove skins. Cut tomatoes in half or fourths and put into large cooking kettle. Add all the blended and chopped ingredients. Cook on medium heat for 3 -3½ hours, stirring every 15 minutes. Do not let burn. When cooked down, bottle in pint jars and process for 20 minutes. The secret is the slow cooking. For milder salsa remove all seeds. (Wear gloves to prevent pepper burns; open window for adequate ventilation.)

Mom's Baked Beans

2 30-oz. cans pork and beans	1 pound fried & chopped bacon
½ c. catsup	1 c. chopped ham (optional)
½ c. cider vinegar	2 T. brown sugar
1 c. chili sauce	¼ c. molasses
1 t. dry mustard	1 can 15-oz. well-drained
1 chopped onion	pineapple chunks (optional)
¼ t. garlic powder	

Place the pork and beans, chopped onion, catsup, vinegar, chili sauce, chopped bacon and ham, mustard, garlic powder, brown sugar and molasses into a Crock-pot and mix well. Cook in Crock-pot for 4-5 hours or until all flavors have mixed into the beans. If you are going to use pineapple, put that into the bean mixture about 1 hour before serving. This recipe can also be baked in a 325° oven for about 2-3 hours.

Easy Sunday Night Supper

Grate one medium size zucchini, one crooked-neck yellow squash, and chop one medium size onion, 1 medium green and/or red pepper, 3 tomatoes, and any other vegetable you wish to add to this mixture. Grate 1½ c. white or yellow cheese. Place the vegetable mixture down the center of a flour tortilla, along with a slice or two of Swiss cheese. You may also place a thin slice of turkey breast and/or thin sliced ham. Sprinkle the grated cheese on top and roll the tortilla into a long length roll. Place on dinner plate and sprinkle a little cheese on top. Heat in the microwave on high for 3 minutes until the vegetables are cooked. Serve with salsa, sliced olives, and sour cream and chips. Add a fruit drink and your supper is prepared in 15 min.

Paul's Quick Roast Beef Dinner

Before leaving for the day, place a small bonless beef roast in oiled Crock-pot. Sprinkle garlic powder on roast. Add 1-2 c. water, 1 small chopped onion, 2 stalks chopped celery, 4-6 scrubbed potatoes, and 4-6 cut carrots. Slow cook for 6 to 8 hours. When arriving home from a busy day of school or work, dinner is ready. (Crock-pot dinners are great for students, busy working people, and tired moms.)

Jennifer's Zucchini Casserole

Layer in oiled casserole dish:

1 med. zucchini
1 med. chopped onion

1 can tomato sauce
1½ cups shredded cheese
    (finishing with cheese on top)

Bake in 325° oven for 30 minutes and serve.

Crispy Chicken Salad

(1)
1 chicken
3 c. shredded lettuce
1 c. mung bean sprouts
2 chopped tomatoes
½ c. chopped celery
5 chopped green onions
1 diced cucumber
1 chopped green pepper

(2)
1 t. salt
1 t. sugar
3 T. vinegar
2 T. soy sauce
2 T. sesame oil
dash of garlic powder

(3)
1 T. sesame seeds
2 T. roasted and ground peanuts (opt.)
1 pkg. won ton skins cut in very thin strips
4 c. cooking oil (for deep fry)

(1) Boil the chicken. Remove, debone and shred. Shred and cut up
    vegetables, keeping them separated.
(2) Mix ingredients in a bowl, adding chopped green pepper and
    shredded chicken. Let sit for few minutes.
(3) Heat 4 c. of oil in a wok or pan. Test oil. Put a strip of won ton
    in oil. If won ton remains at bottom, oil is not hot enough.

Remove strip and continue heating until hot enough. Then place several strips of won ton in for frying. Quickly fry won tons to a golden light brown, remove and drain. Continue until all strips are fried and drained.

(4) Arrange shredded lettuce on large serving platter. Toss remaining vegetables together and place over lettuce. Next place chicken mixture over vegetables. Sprinkle with sesame seeds and roasted peanuts. Top with fried and drained won ton strips, piling high. Remaining won ton strips can be served in a bowl alongside crispy chicken salad platter.

Serves 8-10. A very popular dish, never any leftovers.

Lemon Chicken

(1)
1 lb. boneless chicken breast
1 T. vinegar
3 T. soy sauce
½ t. salt
1/8 t. black pepper
1 egg yolk
2 T. cornstarch

(2)
2 T. flour
5 T. cornstarch

(3)
1 T. oil
1 T. cornstarch
3 T. water
3 T. lemon juice
3 T. sugar
½ t. salt

3 c. oil (for frying)

(1) Remove skin from chicken and cut diagonally into thin slices. Mix other ingredients in a bowl and combine with chicken. Marinate for 1 hour. Remove meat and dredge in mixture #(2).

(2) Preheat pan and add oil. Heat to 375°. Deep-fry chicken for 15-30 seconds and remove. Turn heat to 400° and deep-fry chicken again for just 10 seconds. Remove, drain and place on serving platter.

(3) Heat in a pan 1 T. oil. Add mixture #(3) and bring to boil. Add 1 T. oil. This will give sauce a sheen. Pour sauce over chicken and serve immediately.

Serves 6.

Variation...

For Sweet and Sour Chicken substitute vinegar for lemon juice in mixture #(3) and prepare same recipe as above.

Beef with Broccoli

(1)
1 lb. beef tenderloin
2 T. soy sauce
1 T. grape juice
½ t. baking soda
6 T. water
2 T. cornstarch
1 T. oil

(2)
1 lb. broccoli
6½ in. pieces green onions
6 slices ginger root
1 T. grape juice
2 T. oil

(3)
½ t. sugar
dash pepper
½ t. veg. oil
4 T. water
2 T. cornstarch

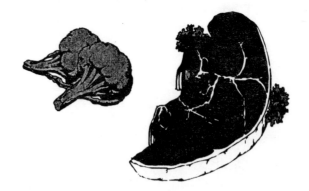

½ c. oil for cooking

(1) Slice beef into thin bite-size pieces, across grain and mix with soy sauce, grape juice, baking soda, water. Next mix in cornstarch and marinate 1 hour. Add 1 T. oil and mix.

(2) Cut broccoli flowerets from stems and separate. Cook for 1-2 minutes in boiling water; remove and drain. Place flowerets on outer edge of serving dish and keep warm. (Broccoli should be bright green.)

(3) Heat wok and add ½ c. oil, heating until hot. Place beef in wok and stir-fry until color changes. Remove and drain. Add 2 T. oil to wok and stir-fry green onions and ginger root until fragrance is noticeable. Add beef and #(3) mixture of sugar, pepper, oil, water, and cornstarch (which has been previously mixed). Stir-fry lightly until mixture thickens. Arrange in the center of the serving platter and serve immediately.

Serves 6.

Stir-Fry Chicken & Pea Pods with Rice

1 c. water	2 T. vegetable oil
1 chicken bouillon cube, crumbled	2 lbs. chicken breasts, skinned, boned & cut in ¾" cubes
2 T. soy sauce	1 T. vegetable oil
1 T. cornstarch	1 6-oz. pkg. frozen Chinese pea pods unthawed or
½ t. garlic salt	equivalant of fresh pods
2 green onions, chopped	1 small can water chestnuts, drained & sliced
3 c. hot cooked brown rice	

Combine in small bowl 1 c. water, bouillon cube, soy sauce, cornstarch, garlic salt and stir until smooth. In a large skillet or wok, heat 2 T. of oil. Add chicken and cook while stirring over high heat until meat is white. This takes 2-3 minutes. Remove chicken from wok and keep warm. Now add 1 T. oil and then add unthawed frozen pea pods or the fresh pea pods and stir until tender, about 2 minutes. Their color will be bright green. Add water chestnuts and cornstarch mixture. Cook and stir until sauce is thick and clear. Add chicken. Have hot cooked rice ready before cooking the chicken and pea pods. When chicken is ready, stir green chopped onions into the hot rice. Place hot cooked rice on large platter and pour chicken and pea pod mixture over hot rice. Serve immediately.

Chicken Broccoli Casserole

5 whole chicken breasts or 1 whole chicken	1 T. lemon juice
	1 c. mayonnaise
2 pkgs frozen cooked & drained broccoli or 2 lb. fresh, steamed & drained broccoli (cook until barely done; will be bright green)	½ to 1 t. curry powder
	3 c. grated mild cheddar cheese
	1½ c. croutons
3 cans cream of chicken soup (broth from chicken can be used)	

Cook and bone chicken, breaking or cutting chicken into pieces. Steam broccoli and drain. Place broccoli on bottom of baking dish (9x13). Next put chicken over broccoli. Combine and heat in a sauce pan the 3 cans cream of chicken soup, adding a little of the broth, 1 T. of lemon juice, 1 c. mayonnaise and ½ to 1 t. curry powder. Stir well and then add 1½ c. grated cheese and stir until melted. Pour sauce over chicken and top with the remainder of the grated cheese and sprinkle the croutons on top. Bake in a 350° oven for 20 minutes. Serve immediately. Do not over bake.

Kristine's Cheese Baked Chicken Breasts

4 large whole boneless, skinless chicken breasts cut in two	¼ c. white grape juice
8 1-oz slices of Swiss cheese	2 c. seasoned stuffing mix (mix seasons with breads)
1 can cream of chicken soup	1/3 c. melted butter
paprika	

Split chicken breasts. Rinse, pat dry and arrange in a 2 quart casserole. Place slice of cheese on each breast. Stir soup and juice together and pour over chicken breasts. Coarsly crush seasoned stuffing mix and sprinkle over the top. Evenly drizzle butter on. Sprinkle top generously with paprika. Bake uncovered at 350° for 45 minutes. A rich cheese sause forms while baking. Serve with rice. Serves 8.

Miriam's Pizza Rolls

1 loaf Rhodes bread dough thawed. Roll on floured surface into rectangle.

Spread 4-oz. softened cream cheese on dough and top with any or all of the following:

1 small can olives chopped	1 c. chopped ham
1 small can mushrooms chopped	1 c. grated mozzarella cheese
1 stick of pepperoni chopped in blender	1 c. chopped pineapple
	1 green pepper chopped
4 chopped green onions	

Roll up and cut in 1" slices as you would cinnamon rolls. Bake at 350° for 12-15 minutes. Before serving, spoon on pizza quick sauce made of 1 can tomato sauce with spaghetti seasoning package mix.

Mignonne's Easy Chicken Wings

Place 5 pounds of chicken wings in Crock-pot. Cover with Yoshida's Original Sauce (purchased in 88-oz. bottle—usually takes about half the bottle). Slow cook in Crock-pot for 4-6 hours or until meat is ready to fall from the bones. Serve on rice. Refrigerate leftover sauce, using for another time.

Potato Casserole

8 medium sized potatoes boiled until not quite done (in their skins). When cooled, peel and grate into large shreds.

Mix:
    ½ c. melted butter
    1 pint sour cream

1 can cream of chicken soup
½ c. green chopped onions
1½ c. shredded cheese

Layer in pan with potatoes first and then sauce and cover top layer with sauce and ½ c. cornflake crumbs and 2 T. melted butter. Use a large pan or baking dish and bake for 30 minutes in a 350° oven.

The Great Baked Potato

Red baked potatoes. Bake in foil until tender.
Serve with the following toppings:

butter	chopped parsley
yogurt (or sour cream)	sunflower seeds
grated cheese	chopped tomato
chopped green onion (or chives)	cottage cheese
bacon bits	Spike and/or salt and pepper

You may put all of these toppings on or use only those you wish. These potatoes are a meal in themselves and a family favorite. I like to use the red potatoes because they are more moist.

Susan's Yam Souffle

3 c. cooked and mashed yams	½ t. salt
1/3 c. margarine (soft)	½ c. brown sugar
1/3 c. orange juice (fresh)	¼ c. plain yogurt
1½ t. grated orange peeling	½ c. milk
1/8 t. nutmeg	3 eggs, beaten
1½ t. vanilla	

Mix all together and bake in oiled 9 x 13 pan and sprinkle the following on top: 1 c. unsweetened coconut 1 c. chopped nuts (pecans or walnuts) ½ c. brown sugar (less if you wish) Bake at 350° for 35-45 minutes

Kristine's Cream Sauce over Pasta & Steamed Vegetables

¼ c. chopped basil	½ c. Parmesan cheese, grated
¼ c. chopped chives	4-6 c. cooked pasta of choice
¼ c. chopped parsley	(spinach is good)
8 oz. cream cheese	1/3 c. ea. diced carrots, chopped
½ c. milk	broccoli, chopped zucchini

Cook pasta according to directions and drain. In separate pan steam the diced and chopped vegetables. Mix pasta and vegetables together.

While vegetables are cooking, saute in 2 T. olive oil; basil, chives, parsley. Break up cream cheese and add to herbs. Add milk and stir until cheese melts. Add grated Parmesan cheese. Serve sauce over pasta and vegetables. Add a little grated Parmesan cheese on top. Garnish with a sprig of fresh parsley.

Rachelle's Herb Garden and Lemon Pasta

8-oz. uncooked twist pasta	¼ c. chopped fresh basil
1/3 c. vegetable oil (olive)	¼ c. chopped fresh chives
3 c. sliced zucchini	¼ c. chopped fresh parsley
(medium size)	2 medium tomatoes cut
1 c. chopped red onion	into wedges
¼ c. freshly grated Parmesan	½ t. salt
cheese-grated	½ t. pepper
2 T. lemon juice	

Cook pasta according to package directions and drain. Meanwhile in 10 inch skillet heat oil, add zucchini and onion. Cook over medium heat, stirring occasionally until zucchini is crisply tender. (5-7 minutes)

Add remaining ingredients and pasta. Cover. Let stand 2 minutes or until tomatoes are heated through. Serve with garlic bread.

Jennifer's Fresh Tomato Spaghetti Sauce

1 c. fresh sliced mushrooms	¼ c. fresh chopped sweet basil
1 med. chopped onion	1 minced clove garlic
2 stalks chopped celery	1 6-oz. can tomato paste
1 grated carrot	6 whole, peeled fresh tomatoes*
1 small grated zucchini	½ lb. cooked extra lean
1 small chopped green pepper	ground beef
¼ c. fresh chopped oregano	3 T. olive oil

In fry pan saute mushrooms, onion, celery, carrot, zucchini, pepper, garlic, and herbs. Remove from pan and place ground beef in and cook. In a separate pan put blended fresh tomatoes, tomato paste and heated vegetables. Bring to boil and reduce to simmer for 1 hour. Add salt and pepper to taste and add cooked ground beef. Let simmer another ½ hour and serve over spaghetti, and top with cheese of your choice.

*When fresh tomatoes are not in season, use 1 quart canned tomatoes, or blend 6 frozen tomatoes in a little water. You can leave the meat out entirely and not even miss it. Serve with garlic bread and Orange Almond Salad. (Root beer floats are a fun desert for us.)

Whole Wheat Pizza

Crust:

1 c. warm water	1 T. honey
1 T. yeast	1 egg
1 t. salt	2½ c. whole wheat flour
1 T. oil	

Topping:

1 can tomato sauce
1 lb. cooked ground beef
½ c. sliced mushrooms
½ c. chopped gr. peppers
½ c. chopped olives
4 c. grated cheese (2 c. Mozarella, 2 c. mild cheddar)

1 small can, well-drained pineapple (optional)
1 pkg. pepperoni
1 pkg. Canadian bacon

Soak yeast, honey in warm water. Add oil, salt, and 1 c. flour. Stir well. Add beaten egg and remainder of flour. (Sometimes you will need a little more flour and sometimes less. It depends upon the humidity and the weather for that day.) Stir very well, making a soft dough. Form into a ball and let rise about ½-1 hour and then knead well.

Roll out dough (enough for 2 pans) and spread over the oiled pizza pan. Bake in hot 400° oven for 10 minutes. Bring out of oven, place the tomato sauce on, and add all the toppings, putting the cheese, pepperoni, Canadian bacon, and ground beef on last. Bake again for 10 additional minutes.

Note: An alternate dough would be 1 c. warm water, 1 t. salt, 1 T. yeast; stir flour into water mixture and form ball. Let rise and roll out.

If you wish to make a vegetable pizza, leave out the ground beef, pepperoni, and Canadian bacon.

Michael's Beef Jerky

1½ t. salt
¼ c. Teriyaki sauce
½ t. white pepper

1 t. garlic powder
2 T. catsup
2 T. Worchestershire Sauce

½ t. liquid smoke   2 lb. lean, thinly sliced beef*
2 T. brown sugar   ¼ c. Soy Sauce
1/8 t. cayenne powder

In a small bowl, mix well all ingredients except for meat. Cut sliced meat into long strips 3/16 to ¼ inch thick. In a shallow dish place meat strips in a single layer. Pour first mixture over meat, making sure both sides of meat are covered with the liquid. Cover tightly and marinate 6 to 12 hours. Stir occasionally. Place meat strips on to dehydrator drying trays and turn dryer controls to 150–160°. Dry for 3–4 hours. Reduce temperature to 130° after 4 hours to finish drying. To make sure the meat is dry, cool a piece and bend it. The meat should crack but not break and there should be no moist spots on the meat. This makes about a half pound of jerky.

*Some meats to use are breakfast steaks, thinly sliced bottom or top of the round of beef. Make sure the meat is very lean.

INDEX OF RECIPES

PART VI

SHARING THE GOOD NEWS

We've talked about the benefits of good deal clubs, and the support and enthusiasm and increased savings that come from joining with friends and relatives and neighbors in applying these Money Savers.

Good news is meant to share. Few people are so well off financially that making ends meet is not a challenge. Saving money is important to thinking, conscientious people everywhere.

Consider your acquaintances—friends, neighbors, relatives, young, old, single, married, retired or newlywed. Which of them could benefit from knowing how to save money by having these proven ways to save big?

Whether talking about the ideas over the back fence or giving the book as a gift, it is a right-good money-saving thing to do—ideas and methods whose time have arrived.

How many people do you know who could benefit from this book and its money saving ideas?